THE PHOTOCO

Britain
Since
1930
ACTIVITY BOOK

Written by Paul Cross
Illustrated by Paul Cross and Paul Sealey

A photocopiable Teacher Resource Book for
Primary classes studying Britain since the 1930's.

Published by
Topical Resources

Britain Since 1930

by _____

Class_____

INTRODUCTION

A Topic is an approach to teaching in a Primary School which involves various apparently unrelated tasks being carried out under the umbrella of a common title or theme such as "Britain Since 1930".

Topic work always:
- Involves class, group and individual work with some elements of choice.
- Involves practical activities.
- Uses themes selected which are thought appropriate to the interests and stages of development of the children involved.
- Involves first hand experiences such as visits or visitors.
- Involves some sort of investigation.
- Involves using investigation gathering skills.
- Crosses some curriculum boundaries.
- It should also include, if possible, an element of "FUN".

The purpose of this book is to provide a bank of ideas and photocopiable activities, based on a Britain Since 1930 Study, which fulfil the above criteria. It is envisaged that the busy class teacher will use his/her professional judgement to select activities appropriate to their own individual situation.

Acknowledgments

The Author and Publishers would like to thank the following for their kind permission to reproduce copyright illustrations: University of Central Lancashire: 16 (below); Costains: 18 (above): Popperfoto: 18 (below), 46 (all), 47 (middle right & bottom), 55 (both); G.E.C./Creda: 22: Daily Express: 25 (above); Imperial War Museum: 25 (below), 34,35, 36 (top right & both bottom); Kent Messenger: 27 & 29 (all); Ministry of Agriculture: 36 (top left); Crompton Lighting Ltd.: 38 (top left); The Advertising Archive Ltd.: 38 (top right & bottom left); Bisto - a registered trademark of R.H.M. Foods: 38 (bottom right); Lancashire Evening Post: 39 (both), 40 (middle), 41 (bottom); Lancashire County Council: 40 (top & bottom); The Hulton Getty Picture collection Ltd.: 47 (top); Mirror Syndication: 47 (middle left);

The publishers have endeavoured to trace the copyright holders of all illustrations in this publication. If we have unwittingly infringed copyright, we sincerely apologise, and will be pleased, on being satisfied as to the owner's title, to pay an appropriate fee as if we had been able to obtain prior permission.

CONTENTS

Copyright © 1997 Paul Cross
Illustrated by Paul Cross.&.Paul Sealey

Printed in Great Britain for "Topical Resources", Publishers of Educational Materials, P.O.Box 329, Broughton, Preston. PR3 5LT (Tel./Fax. 01772 863158) by T.Snape & Company Ltd., Boltons Court, Preston.

Cover by Paul Sealey Illustration & Design.
First Published January 1997
ISBN 1 872977 11 1

Political and Economic Change in Britain in the 1930's

This period saw the most rapid and radical change in Britain's history.After the First World War there were great expectations of a better life for everyone in Britain.Prime Minister Lloyd George had promised everyone a land fit for heroes.But the war had caused inflation. Some of the countries who had been customers for British goods now had little money to buy those goods after the war.Other countries had become more competitive and were importing fewer British goods and seeking to sell their goods in Britain cheaper than home made goods. Old industries like ship building and coal mining struggled, and only a few new light industries like electrical goods managed to prosper.

The Wall Street economic collapse of 1929 led to a slump in world trade which brought the terrible economic depression and unemployment of the 1930's.Lack of demand for British goods both at home and abroad meant that industries had to lay off workers and factories had to close. Conservative Labour and Coalition Governments all struggled with the situation whilst unemployment rose to over 3 million.Similar situations in European countries saw severe social and political unrest,with conflict between Communist and nationalist or Fascist parties such as those in Italy,Germany and Spain. Strife in the latter country eventually developed into a brutal civil war in 1937.

Whilst there were marches and riots between the Fascist party of Oswald Mosley and communists and socialists Britain kept to her democratic form of government. The fascist Italian and German dictatorships were keen to assert their nationalism and began to arm themselves in preparation for the invasion of nearby states.The build up of their armies, airforces, and navies was greeted in the late 1930's by the "appeasement" policies of the Government Neville Chamberlain. He advocated giving the Fascist governments a little land to satisfy their demands.The failure of this policy was swiftly followed by rapid rearmament in Britain early in 1939 and a subsequent improvement in the economic and political life of Britain.

The Home Front

The advances in warfare meant that during war ever person in Britain felt part of the war. All experienced knew someone who experienced evacuation, ga masks, the blackout, rationing, bombing, relative fighting in the services,changes in employmen saving or salvage campaigns, loss of family membe in battle or as prisoners or some form deprivation.This was the first war in which ever person felt they were fighting in the war. Theirs was th "Home Front"

The Course of the War

When Hitler's Germany invaded Poland Britain alor with France honoured their promises to the Poles ar declared war on Germany.The British troops rushed France, experienced a "Phoney war" for a few month before the onslaught of the German "blitzkrieg".Th invasion of Denmark and Norway lead to the downfa of Chamberlain's Conservative Government and th formation of a Government of the National Intere under Winston Churchill. However the ne Government faced severe difficulties as Hollan Belgium and France were soon invaded by th Germans.

The British Army seemed doomed and marooned the sand dunes of Dunkirk. The miraculous rescue over 400,000 men was heralded as a triumph for th small boat flotilla and the Government. The fact that the army's equipment was left in France clouded th triumph.Hitler's attempts to bring Britain to surrend and his Blitz bombing of London and other maj British cities were supposed to precede a Germa invasion of Britain.

The R.A.F.fighter pilots part in deterring Hitler invasion plan meant that the Government were given breathing space to reorganise and regroup. Th National Government mobilised the whole nation. Th "Dig for Victory",the salvage and saving campaign the reorganisation of the whole workforce to th production of war goods were brilliantly lead by suc varied personalities as Beaverbrook, Erne Bevin,Morrison and Atlee. All this was accomplishe with an enormous effort in Propaganda inform,persuade and enthuse the population in cooperation with the Government.

The Japanese attack on Pearl Harbour in 1941, meant that the war now became global with America reacting immediately to an attack on their land. Hitler's invasion of Russia led to a British alliance with the communist state and a world war. The member countries of the British Empire all had forces involved with British and American forces in the campaigns in North Africa, the invasion of Italy, the huge "D" day invasion of France, and the eventual victory in Europe in May 1945.

The British Empire and the American forces combined in campaigns in Burma, Malaya and the Pacific Ocean against the Japanese forces. The Atomic Bombs dropped on Hiroshima and Nagasaki in Japan meant not only the end of the war with Japan but also the start of an age of fear of the ultimate war weapon.

Post War Britain

Churchill's and the Conservatives defeat in the 1945 election brought in a period of political and social change under the Labour Party. The nationalisation of Coal, Power, the Railways, the Docks and the Health service as well as the 1944 Education Act radically changed the political and economic life of Britain. These nationalisations were carried forward in a period of severe deprivation and economic stagnation which followed the war.

This was a period when rationing was stricter than during the war. The late 1940's were a period of austerity and very slow economic recovery. This was caused by industries which desperately needed re-equipping with modern machinery not having the investment or incentives to do so. The pacts made between Roosevelt (U.S.A.), Stalin (U.S.S.R.), and Churchill in wartime had sought to divide Europe in peace in an amicable way.

The Communist take over of Eastern Europe meant that a state of readiness for war against the opposing "bloc" dominated the early post war years leading to the need to keep large conscripted and armed forces to defend Western Europe. Faced with these problems the British economy was slower to recover than many economies. This slow recovery and economic stagnation meant that many skilled workers sought a better life in the Americas and Australia.

When the British economy did recover in the middle 1950's there was a sudden demand for cheap unskilled workers. Industries and services drew upon immigrant workers from the former colonies of the Indian subcontinent and the Caribbean islands. This period of prosperity was followed by inflation in the early 1960's. This in turn was followed by a short boom then more inflation and severe industrial unrest in the later 1970's.

The early 1980's saw a severe reorganisation of industry and large scale unemployment through the need to re-equip and modernise British industry. This was accompanied by the dismantling of many of the industries nationalised in the 1940's and the privatisation of these industries. The late 1980's were a period of economic well being for many with a contrasting unemployment for up to 3 million people. Since 1945 Britain has seen a very rapid increase in crime and violence which would have scandalised earlier generations. At the same time as these radical changes the British Empire was changing as colonies in Asia and Africa became independent and lessened their dependence on Britain. The development of the European Common Market and Britain's membership of it has brought about a change in the way Britain trades and considers itself in the the world and a shifting of the areas to which Britain exported its goods. Before 1950 the British economy had relied upon the "Empire" and America for 70 per cent of its exports, after 1980 Europe was the market place for 60 per cent of Britain's exports. The changes in the British economy in the 1970's and 1980's meant that Britain became viewed as an ideal base for Far Eastern and American businesses to gain entry into the European market by building factories and assembly plants in areas of economic decline such as Tyneside and Wales. Here they could draw on a workforce eager to adapt to new skills.

In the military field since 1945 British forces have been engaged in military action or defence in Germany, Korea, Cyprus, the Congo, the Arabian Gulf states and Bosnia as part of the United Nations or Nato forces aimed at preserving peace in the world or defending the West against a perceived threat of communism.

Social and Domestic Changes Since 1930

The 1930's were a period of rapid change in the towns and countryside of Britain. Despite the depression more than 2 million new homes were built in Britain in the 1930's. These homes were built on the edge of towns forming the suburbs of semi-detached and detached houses which still ring most British towns. These suburbs needed new transport systems to ferry the mainly male commuters into work. Hence the train, bus and underground commuter routes of modern day Britain.

The development of the modern cheap family car meant that suburban dwellers headed the revolution in the leisure use of the motor car. The weekend traffic jams on the inadequate roads leading to the seaside resorts and major countryside attractions were mainly caused by these suburban motorists. The new homes all advertised that they were equipped with the very latest labour saving electrical and gas appliances. These appliances gave the suburban housewife more leisure time freeing them from the household drudgery.

Their leisure time was spent in sports like tennis, golf and bowls; activity groups such as the W.I., and shopping expeditions to the local town, followed by tea and cakes with friends in one of the teashops that each town sprouted in the 1930's. The lives of these suburbanites are chronicled by Betjeman's poems.

By contrast the families of working class people faced severe conditions in the 1930's with poor housing giving women a life of domestic drudgery. Unemployment brought the ignominy of the "Means Test" officer's visit to their homes. His job was to deny the "dole" money to anyone with any possession that could be sold.

Local authorities sought to alleviate this problem by using the unemployed in civic road, parks and house building projects. Cities and towns sought to help their poor slum dwellers by building cheap homes with gardens for rent on the edge of towns.

The onset of war halted this state of local governmental help. The building of cheap homes for rent was only renewed with the Prefabricated bungalows and semi detached council estates of the late 40's and early 50's. These were extended a prosperity brought councils the money to rehous poorer slum dwellers in the high rise "flats" of th 1960's and the vast social deserts of the housin estates far from city centres or other civic amenities.

The division of classes was emphasised in all thes social and domestic developments in the 1930's. Th private estates were marked by individual adaptatic of their homes that only came to the council rente properties with privatisation of the 1980's.

Technological Changes Radically Change the Social Habits of Britain From 1930

The cinema and the radio which enjoyed hug popularity throughout the 1930's and 1940's wer forces which tended to unite most classes in the leisure time. Music, news, drama and comed programmes were listened to by huge nation wid audiences in their own homes. The cinema boom sa large towns with up to 30 separate cinemas, eac showing several different films each week to packe audiences. This was a total change to many people social life.

A national television service changed the social habi of the nation wiping out the cinemas domination of leisure time. With the advent of commercial televisio in the late 1950's and its extension with first vide recorders and then satellite T.V. in the 1980's ar 1990's the leisure habits of the British people we radically changed. The average British househo were watching 5 hours of television each day

The development in computers, started in the 1970' further revolutionised British homes and business as the computer came to dominate both commerc and the home games sectors of life.

The introduction of the supermarket concept shopping in the early 1960's and the move to bu super stores on the edge of towns changed people shopping habits. But the most radical social change the later part of the 20th century was the huge grow of car ownership.

By the 1990's the motor car dominated most people's lives as well as invading vast areas of land through motorways and bypasses that sought to ease the flow of motor vehicles. The huge increases in road traffic lead to daily stagnation at busy sections of roads at peak travel times.The motorcar altered many people's holiday horizons giving a freedom to roam Britain and the continent for their holiday.

However the invention of the jet engine and its extension to large scale passenger aeroplanes has played the most important part in changing the holiday patterns of the British people.

From the early 1960's the"package" holiday traffic has extended the British holiday maker's horizons first to the Mediterranean,then America and Africa and finally to Asia. Many of these holiday makers have returned to Britain with an appetite for foreign and exotic foods.They have provided an eager clientele for the many ethnic and European restaurants and fast food outlets that are a feature of most towns and cities in the late 1990's.

More Leisure Time and Technological Advances Mean Changes in Sporting Activities

The 1930's saw huge crowds watching football and cricket matches each Saturday in winter and summer respectively. The crowd records for both these sports were set on 1930's Saturdays. Following the war these sports predominated until prosperity gave many people greater leisure time,which they began to use in a wider variety of sporting activities. Thus swimming, tennis, rugby, golf, ice hockey, indoor bowling, motor racing and jogging all became popular participant sports from 1950 to 1990.When many of these sports were televised their popularity grew, as did their commercial pulling power.

The introduction of sponsorship to advertise a company's goods on hoardings, equipment and players shirts was a product of the increasing sports exposure on television.The extra cash attracted to sports by television exposure and its impact on a sport

are epitomised by the growth in snooker's popularity and its players increasing wages from 1930 to 1990.

In 1930 snooker attracted few spectators to working men's clubs. By 1990, millions were viewing it on television and thousands attending its tournaments in principal theatres throughout the land.
Participation in sports such as swimming, jogging weight training and aerobics became very popular with the linking of health problems to lack of exercise.Sports centres and swimming pools were built from the late 1960's onwards to cater for these new leisure pursuits.

The 1930's had seen organised mass protests on private moorlands as ramblers sought the right to walk over the natural beauty spots of Britain.The hills and countryside of Britain are now riddled with long distance way marked pathways as a consequence of these early actions by country loving exercise seeking people.

The Development of the Popular Musical Industry

Radio brought modern musical songs to millions of homes in the 1930's and 40's.Thousands flocked to buy sheet music of the latest popular tune to play on their own pianos.During the war the songs of Vera Lynne, Gracie Fields and George Formby brought comedy and romance to many separated by the conflict.

The American troops brought the "jive" to dance halls throughout the war. After the war in the 1950's "Rock and Roll" music made world "pop" stars of Bill Haley, Little Richard and Elvis Presley. These singers sold records by the thousands and in the 1960's British Pop stars such as The Beatles and the Rolling stones made millions from their world popularity. A Whole T.V., Film and recording industry grew up which by the late 1990's was the country's fifth largest export industry.

Homes and Buildings

Teach children to look out for the semi-detached houses with their plaster and timber gables. Children will enjoy copying their style in mock adverts for their sale in leafy suburban landscapes.

Copies of the 1930's stained glass windows from semi detached homes with their floral and landscape themes could highlight classroom windows.

The Anderson shelter in its surrounding "Dig for Victory" garden and the Prefabricated homes of the late 1940's make ideal 3D projects which can be made in scrap and corrugated card.

The rectangular starkness of 1960's high rise flats and office blocks made from cereal boxes will provide a geometric contrast to more adventurous building designs like the Liverpool Metropolitan Cathedral, the Post Office Tower and many 1960's modern churches created from different shaped packaging.

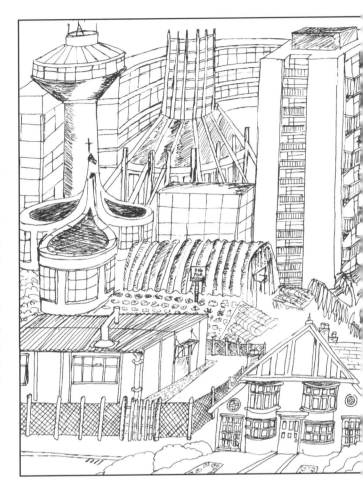

TRAVEL CHEAPLY BY L.N.E.R.

The Age of the Poster.

Copies of 1930's travel or holiday posters giv excellent opportunities for children to explore th art of water colour landscape painting with their use c bold colours. Their lettering will teach children the a of effective message design.

The propaganda posters of the 2nd World War giv many chances to study the use of wit, simplicity c design and use of few colours to achieve a vita message.

The development of the advertising slogan can b studied through adverts for the same product fror posters of each decade. This would make an excellen classroom display of change and continuity in Art.

The War Artists

Henry Moore's contour filled studies of London Underground shelter dwellers in 1940 provide excellent examples of human form portrayal. They can be drawn in wax crayon and then overpainted with a dark colour wash. They could also give children opportunities for modelling in plasticine or clay.

The brightly coloured pictures of women in wartime by Laura Knight can be contrasted with Stanley Spencer's stylised portrayal of shipwrights of the Clyde. Children will appreciate the detail of the worker's clothes in these pictures. Both could be copied in paper and material collage.

Children's copies of Edward Ardizonne's sketches of life on the Home front can be contrasted by copies of Giles and David Low's cartoons. Children will enjoy their humour and simple line drawings.

The Age of the Comic

Display colour copies of such comic classics as Tiger Tim, Billy Bunter, Girl's school stories, Dennis the Menace, The Bash St Kids, Roy of the Rovers, Dan Dare and Micky Mouse.

Give children their own A3 sheet on which to copy and develop their own comic characters. They will love it !

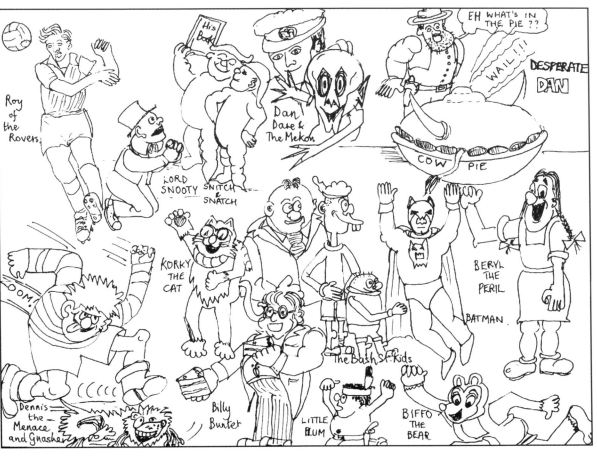

Modern Art

Paul Klee's use of geometric shapes of tonal colours in his portraits and landscapes are wonderful starting points for children to use tones of basic colours. The Surrealist art of Salvador Dali's melting clocks and figures in desert landscape can be used to inspire a child's own dream paintings. Picasso's "Guernica" can be used to study how he explodes the human and other frames to match the horror of "BlitzKrieg."

Children can cut up figures, furniture, buildings and artifacts and recreate their own "Guernica." Picasso's animal sculptures can be inspirational sources for the children's sculptures in clay, plasticine and scrap materials. The drawings and paintings of Graham Sutherland based on twigs and beach debris give excellent opportunities for children's observational drawings. Andy Warhol's use of repetitive poster techniques using soup and bean tins,or film stars give excellent models for children's posters of household goods or modern "pop" idols. The outrageous splash art of Pollock with its bright colours excites children to produce weird designs which they will enjoy christening with their own titles. Visits to any local Museum with examples of Art of the later part of the 20th Century would illuminate any study of Britain Since 1930.

Art Deco Buildings

Cinemas and Cafe frontages, large cit department stores and the fla roofed,curved windows of 1930s houses ca be used to give children the chance to be designer.

Give them a variety of shapes to fit into the design and they will produce their own "A Deco" buildings.

Art Deco Statues and Sculptures

Small decorative figures of dancing girls draped in flowing dresses balanced on rocks or obelisks give opportunities for children to draw the human figure in movement. Children could model the smooth shapes of large cats, birds and fish in the flowing Art Deco animal movement sculpture.

Art Deco Ceramics

The pottery of this period has many different shapes and is decorated with stylised floral, landscape, bird, animal and geometric designs. Children can copy these patterns onto prepared shapes which copy the wide range of Art Deco pottery shapes.

Slab pots could be made of the more geometric shapes such as teapots or plates, which children will enjoy colouring in vivid colours.

Transport Art

Cars, lorries, tractors, trains and motor bikes have changed radically since 1930. The design styles of land transport will provide a superb classroom display. Flying above this could be suspended mobiles of card shapes of airships, aeroplanes, helicopters and spacecraft to fit in with the time scale. Add the vast range of liners, warships, submarines and hovercrafts built since the 1930's and the classroom will have a transport time line.

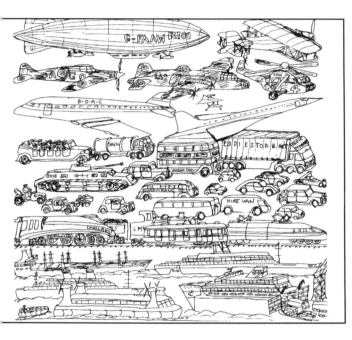

Art in Fashion

Set groups of children to research the male and female fashions of a decade. Their designs produced as 3D replica models can be put together to display 60 years of popular fashion's change and continuity.

Film Art

Children's research into the films and filmstars since 1930 will provide lots of colourful images for the class to produce a collage of children's film art ideas as a class display. Masks of various film stars would add a border to the work.

Notes for Teachers

page:

14. As well as being an activity that pupils will enjoy when well prepared this could provide an effective part of the school's community relations programme.

15. This document gives the chance to show how Global Events can affect local people.

16. The extracts from the diary could form a contrasting reference to any interviews with old people undertaken from page 14. A passage where children should be taught to shift the information to select relevant facts.

17. Personal accounts that can be studied to discover different views of the same historical event. With more able pupils they could be used to detect bias in a person's account of history.

18. This exercise can provide the starting point for a study of the local built environment to date its different types of houses. A useful contrast can be made by studying the property pages of a present day newspaper.

19. As well as being a useful study of different historical sources, this activity could be the starting point for a conversation with a person with memories of the 1930's and 1940's.

20-21 A chance to replicate a 3D shape in every classroom without need for any specialist equipment. Children will enjoy the bold colours and curving designs of Clarice Cliff.

22. An opportunity to study the impact of electricity in the domestic field. An exercise in recognising change and its social impact.

23. A simple but effective way to introduce the causes of the Second World War.

24. A simple cut and paste chronological exercise which can be extended by more advanced pupil's own research.

25. A selective exercise which older schools may be able to extend with research of their own Logbooks for facts about the Home Front.

26. A humourous chance to practice the children's ability to extract facts from different sources.

27. A pleasurable observational exercise that can lead from discussion to individual interpretation.

28. A C.D.T. project that will give children pleasure from recreating history with their hands.

29-30. Contemporary documents giving chances for children to use their interpretive and reasoning skills.

31-33. A stick and paste activity that gives children the chance to practice their chronological skills.

34-35. This study of women's role in the war gives children a chance to practice their reasoning skills.

36. An observational exercise that affords a chance for the development of children's interpretive skills.

37. A classroom display can be made from the children's art work in this activity. The material will provide an excellent topic for conversations with older people.

38. An observational exercise that presents the chance to study a wide range of contemporary source material.

39. A cause and effect exercise that could be contrasted with excerpts from present day newspaper articles about the National Health Service.

40-41. Exercises in change and continuity that chronicles the car's impact on British society since 1930.

42-43. A cut and paste exercise that gives children practice in contrasting different historical sources.

44-45. Children will enjoy using their observational skills to gather and select information from rooms reflecting different domestic scenes since 1930.

46 The early pop industry in Britain gives chances for children to use their reasoning skills.

47 An interpretive exercise that charts the impact of television on Britain's sporting activities.

48 The children's posters of the different decades of fashion will provide an superb class wall display.

49 A selective exercise about flying events since 1930 that could be a starting point for interested pupils to pursue an individual topic.

50-51. Two documents that study the reasons behind people's motives for moving to a different culture. A useful exercise for children to realise other's different cultural backgrounds.

52-53. A game that should be played after children have studied the artifacts of the period, it will exercise their reasoning and debating skills.

54. A cut and paste chronological exercise that uses space exploration for its facts.

55. Children will enjoy inventing their own comic relief activities. The page could be used to arouse interest and ideas for any charitable event linked to school or the local community.

56-59. Levelled worksheets based on Radio, T.V. and the Cinema, giving differentiated work for different groups within the class whilst keeping to the same basic content and line drawings.

60-63. As above but on the theme of Winston Churchill, a famous person from history, who is also an appropriate person to study with KS1 children in a Cross phase class.

Photocopiable Worksheets & Activities

How to Gather Oral Evidence

Interviewing older adults can provide a valuable collection of information about events and life styles of the past. They will give you a lively insight into the past as well as encouraging links with the wider community around the school. A visit to their home or an interview in a relaxed and quiet place in school should be arranged.

How to Arrange an Interview

The wardens of local sheltered housing or local Age Concern clubs, adverts in the local church magazines, and school newsletters may suggest names of people who were youngsters or adults in the Second World War or before.

A suitable place and time for the interview, where you feel the adult will feel relaxed, should be fixed up with help from your teacher. Be kind and thoughtful with the older adult and you will achieve the best climate for your interview. Make sure the person who you are going to interview knows the period you would most like them to talk to you about.

Equipment You May Need

1. A list of prepared questions.
2. A portable tape recorder,with fresh batteries or a lead that is long enough to reach the socket in the place of interview.
3. A microphone which works with the tape recorder you are using.
4. A clip board, paper and pencil for any notes you may need.
5. A karaoke machine attached to the tape recorder will amplify the questions and answers which helps with any hearing problems.
6. A book with pictures of the period you want to discuss may help the answers to flow more freely.
7. Your questions written out so that you know what to ask next. These questions could be given to the person you are going to interview in advance of the interview.

Some ideas for Questions

1) Where did you live when you were a child.?
2) What sort of house did you live in as a child ?
3) How many children were there in your family ?
4) How did your family cook, wash and heat you home ?
5) What did you do in your leisure time as a child?
6) Please could you tell us about your school days?
7) What can you remember about war time rationing'
8) Can you tell us about air raids and shelters in the war?
9) Can you tell us about any different jobs women did in the war?
10) Can you tell us about any member of your family who was involved in the forces in the war?

Task:

1. Design and make a set of questions to ask older members of your family or community.
2. Arrange a meeting and carry out an interview.
3. Make a display of information collected.

Change in the 1930's

I know 3 Trades
I speak 3 Languages
I fought for 3 Years
I have 3 Children
And NO work for 3 months
But I only want
ONE JOB

What had caused this change?
Why had so many people no job?

The man with the Sandwich board above came from the North of England. Although he had many skills he still could not get a job. In the 1930's there were over 2 Million people like him, unemployed, with NO JOB. There had never been so many people without a job.

The Slump.

Before 1930 Britain had made most of the goods used in every British home, and had sent goods such as clothes, shoes, ships, pottery, machines and metalware all over the world. During the 1930's people in other countries did not have enough money to buy British goods. Many more countries began to make their own goods which meant less trade for Britain. So British Factories and works suffered from a SLUMP in trade.

Building Ships

People on the Clyde, near Glasgow, on the Tyne near Newcastle, on the Mersey near Liverpool, and in Belfast had for years made huge ships from steel. They were skilled and built very good ships. But in the 1930's no one wanted any new ships. There was a Slump in the shipping, SO the Ship building owners could not sell their ships, SO they could not pay the Men's wages, SO the men had NO JOBS.

Cotton Mills

Many cotton workers in Lancashire lost their jobs because people in India, Japan and China bought new machines made in Lancashire and began making their own cotton into clothes. These were cheaper than the goods made on old machines in Lancashire. SO Lancashire millowners had to sack some of their workers. SO many Lancashire cotton workers had NO JOBS.

Coal Mining.

There were many coal mines in South Wales, Yorkshire, Scotland, Lancashire and the Midlands in the 1930's. Coal provided the fuel for the steam engines which powered the trains and factories. It was used to heat most people's homes. When factories closed, fewer goods were being carried on the railways and people without jobs could not afford as much coal to heat their homes. SO less coal was needed, SO mine owners sacked many of their coal miners, SO many miners had NO JOB.

Task: Cause and Effect

Unemployment in the 1930's
1. Write out two reasons why you think there was a Slump in trade in the 1930's.
2. Find 2 reasons why you think some coal miners lost their jobs.
3. Give two reasons why you think cotton workers lost their jobs.
4. Why do you think many shipyard workers lost their jobs ?

Interpreting the Evidence
On a map of Great Britain mark the words miners, shipyard workers, and cotton workers in the areas where you think these workers lost their jobs in the 1930's.

The Depression

Nora Pickering's Diary

Nora Pickering born 1915 in Barnoldswick, Lancashire, to a pair of mill workers.

1929

First holiday in Blackpool, Dad takes our picture with a Brownie camera and develops the films himself. I started work at the Scientific Corsetry works at 8 shillings per week as a machinist. I was given sixpence a week spending money.

1930

My sister Hilda aged 9, had tonsillitis, had an operation and was very ill for many months. The Doctor's collector used to call for 1 shilling per week, as we could not afford the doctor's bills. Mother had to go back to working in the Mill to pay the bills and I stayed at home to nurse Hilda. I lost my job and when Hilda was better I had to go into the Cotton Mill and learn to weave. I hated it but there was nothing else. I cried every night; the noise of the machinery was frightening, I got used to it. I had to!

1931

There was a cotton mill strike; the mill owners wanted us to work on 6 looms instead of 4 for the same pay. We had to walk through hundreds of people to get to work and we were kicked, punched and jostled. Eventually everybody was out because the owners locked us out! It lasted for several weeks and there came a time when there was no money for food. So the Weaver's Union official, Mr Lord, came round with vouchers which we changed for food. We were very thankful for them. Also the Salvation Army provided soup for us. I can remember going with a container and being asked how many of a family we were and on saying "Four of us". I was given fou ladles of soup. The mill owners won so we all had to go back to work on 6 looms instead of 4. It was hard work!

Task 1: Selecting information

1. After reading the passage carefully, write out 5 sentences that tell you the Pickering family were quite poor and could not always pay for everything they needed.
2. Write out any sentences that you can find in the passage that tell you that sometimes the Pickering family had spare money.

Task 2: Cause and effect

1. Why do you think that Nora was punched and kicked by hundreds of people as she went to work in 1931?
2. Why do you think the mill owners wanted them to work on 6 looms instead of 4 looms?

Task 3: Information from pictures

Look carefully at the pictures, then choose a sentence from the passage that best fits the picture. Make your own copy of the picture and write the sentence as a title.

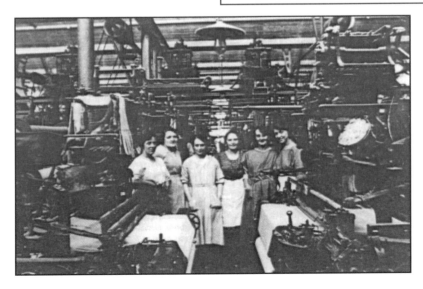

Hunger Marches 1932

A housewife from the Midlands tells of the Jarrow Marchers passing her door on their way to London.

It was a miserable wet day and I heard the sound of Mouth organ music. I rushed out in time to watch the Jarrow Crusade Banner pass and the men so thin. I felt so sad seeing them so hungry looking. I rushed back inside and fetched them two loaves of bread, a pound of sugar and a quarter of tea. I just pushed them into a man's hands and burst out crying. He just said, "Bless you Mam", and marched on.

An unemployed worker from Jarrow remembers.

The shipyard had no orders so we labourers were put out of work. We had no savings so I applied for the "dole." A fellow from the office came to our house and said, "You have plenty of goods. Sell that picture and those ornaments and that piano". He wouldn't give us any money till I'd sold all our possessions. The wife were in tears. She'd saved hard for the few extras we had."

A Sussex Landowner's wife remembers a special visit to London 1932.

We were going up to London for Marjorie Mason's daughter's Coming out Ball. We were on our way there when our Taxi-cab's way was blocked by those awful, dirty Jarrow marchers. My Arnold said that a proper spell of hunger would make them work harder and so keep their shipyards open. Aubrey said that the Government should have arrested them as beggars

Task: Different ways of interpreting the same event

Choose one of the passages above and write a short play script about that person and the Hunger March 1932. Carefully illustrate your script.

New Homes in the 1930's

3 Million new houses built in the 1930's

Many of the old Victorian Terraced houses were knocked down in the 1930s and new housing estates were built on the outskirts of many towns. These new suburbs were mainly homes for sale though many councils built large estates on the edges of their towns and cities for people to rent at reasonable rates.

Task: A reasoning exercise.

Divide a piece of writing paper in half length ways, put neat titles of ADVANTAGES on one side and DISADVANTAGES on the other.

Underneath these titles list the good and bad points of living in new houses in the suburbs. Also list the good and bad points of living in rented or owned new houses.

Research. Look for houses, with similar design to the advert above, near your own school. Find out when they were built and if they were rented or owned. Draw the design of one of these houses.

Entertainment in the 1930's

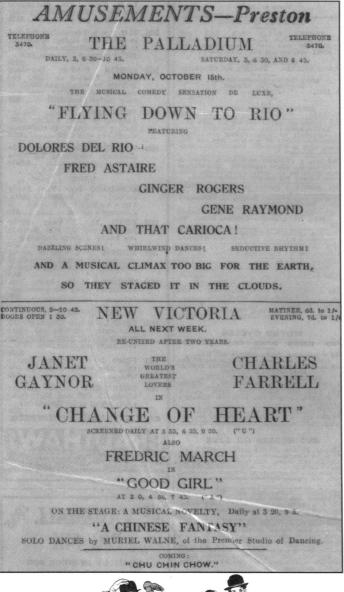

Task 1: Interpreting evidence.

1) How many cinemas does this document suggest there were in Preston in 1934?
2) How many different films could you see in this one week in Preston in 1934?

Task 2: Charting change over 60 years

1) Look in the local paper of your nearest large town, and list the number of films and cinemas that you can see in one week nowadays. List any changes and similarities from 1934 Preston that you discover.

19

Make a 1930's Clarice Cliff Tea Set

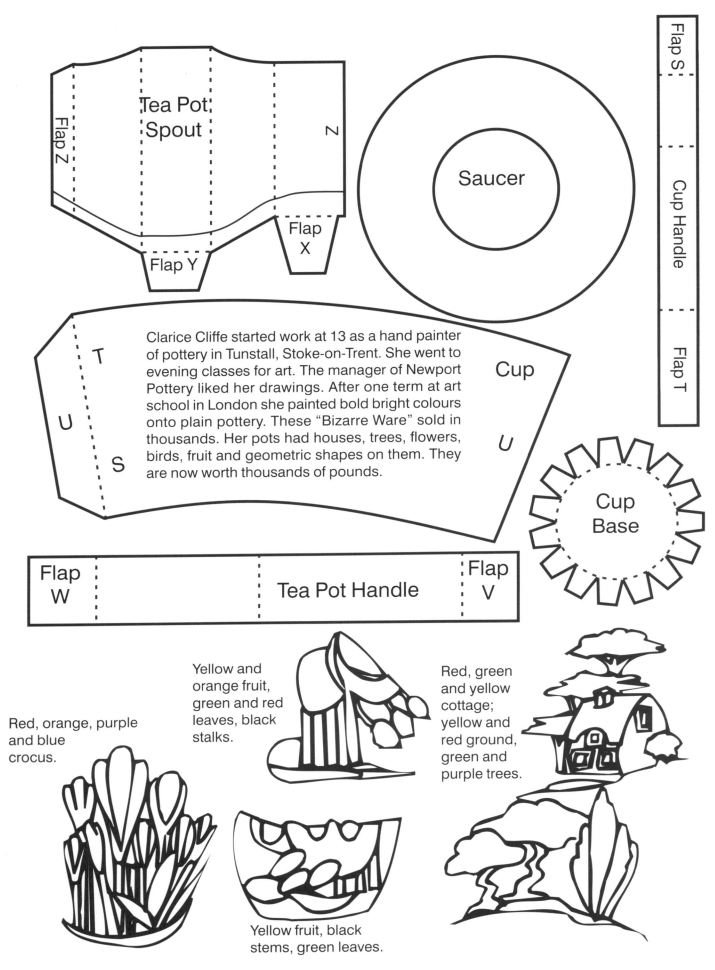

Flap S

Cup Handle

Flap T

Flap Z

Tea Pot Spout

Z

Flap Y

Flap X

Saucer

T

U

S

Clarice Cliffe started work at 13 as a hand painter of pottery in Tunstall, Stoke-on-Trent. She went to evening classes for art. The manager of Newport Pottery liked her drawings. After one term at art school in London she painted bold bright colours onto plain pottery. These "Bizarre Ware" sold in thousands. Her pots had houses, trees, flowers, birds, fruit and geometric shapes on them. They are now worth thousands of pounds.

Cup

U

Cup Base

Flap W

Tea Pot Handle

Flap V

Yellow and orange fruit, green and red leaves, black stalks.

Red, green and yellow cottage; yellow and red ground, green and purple trees.

Red, orange, purple and blue crocus.

Yellow fruit, black stems, green leaves.

Make a 1930's Clarice Cliff Tea Set

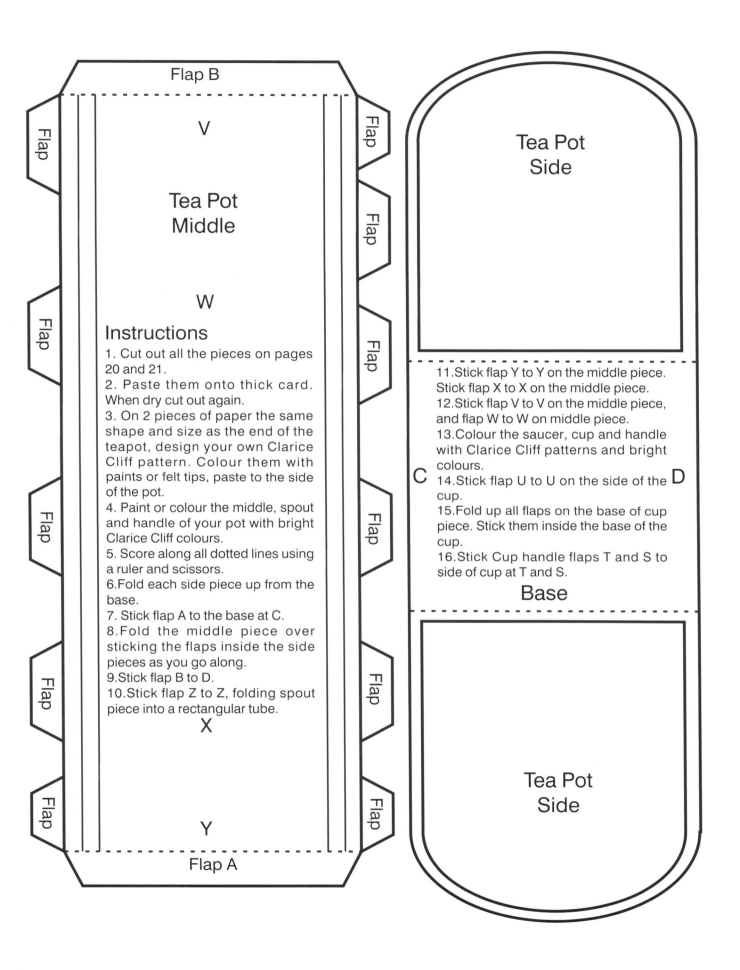

Flap B

V

Tea Pot Middle

W

Flap

Flap

Flap

Flap

Flap

Instructions

1. Cut out all the pieces on pages 20 and 21.
2. Paste them onto thick card. When dry cut out again.
3. On 2 pieces of paper the same shape and size as the end of the teapot, design your own Clarice Cliff pattern. Colour them with paints or felt tips, paste to the side of the pot.
4. Paint or colour the middle, spout and handle of your pot with bright Clarice Cliff colours.
5. Score along all dotted lines using a ruler and scissors.
6. Fold each side piece up from the base.
7. Stick flap A to the base at C.
8. Fold the middle piece over sticking the flaps inside the side pieces as you go along.
9. Stick flap B to D.
10. Stick flap Z to Z, folding spout piece into a rectangular tube.

X

Y

Flap A

Tea Pot Side

Flap

Flap

Flap

Flap

Flap

11. Stick flap Y to Y on the middle piece. Stick flap X to X on the middle piece.
12. Stick flap V to V on the middle piece, and flap W to W on middle piece.
13. Colour the saucer, cup and handle with Clarice Cliff patterns and bright colours.
14. Stick flap U to U on the side of the cup.
15. Fold up all flaps on the base of cup piece. Stick them inside the base of the cup.
16. Stick Cup handle flaps T and S to side of cup at T and S.

C

D

Base

Tea Pot Side

Electricity in the 1930's

Electricity saves time in the home

In 1922 there were 2 million homes in Britain which had an electricity supply. In 1939 there were 11 million homes with an electricity supply. Most of the electricity in Britain in 1930 was generated by coal powered generators.

Task 1: Listing Change

1. Write out what you think each appliance numbered in the advert is called and what it is used for.
2. For each appliance numbered in the advert write down what you think people would use if they could not afford electricity, or electrical appliances.
3. List all the electrical appliances, games, etc you have in your home today. Compare your list with the advert.

Task 2: Reasoning

1. Why do you think that 1930's Housewives longed for a Vacuum cleaner?
2. Why do you think that 1930's women wanted Electric cookers?

© Topical Resources. May be photocopied for classroom use only.

Changes in Europe Affect Britain in the 1930's

Adolf Hitler had been a soldier in the German army in the First World War(1914 to 1918). He hated being beaten and he wanted to make Germany the Greatest Country in the world.

Benito Mussolini had been a soldier in the Italian army in the First World War. He too hated being beaten and wanted to make Italy a great country again.

They both started to lead people in parties called Fascists. They quickly had a large following and became leaders of their countries.

Adolf Hitler

Benito Mussolini

The Fascist's Ideas

(1) To provide work for the unemployed in their countries making new roads, railways, factories and houses.
(2) To build up their armies, navies and airforces to frighten neighbouring countries.
(3) To take over other countries to provide more space for their people.
(4) To harshly treat many minority groups in their country and blame them for the bad state of their country.
(5) To have only their party in the country so that they could rule as they wanted.

The Effect on Britain

- Oswald Mosley started a Fascist party called the Black Shirts. They beat up their opponents and smashed Jewish shops and works.
- Some people wanted Britain to build up its Armed Forces to halt the European Fascists.
- Other people wanted to let the Fascists in Italy and Germany have more land so that they would be satisfied.
- Many German Jews fled from their country and came to live in Britain.

Oswald Mosley

Task: Is this evidence complete or reliable?

Write True or False or the Evidence doesn't tell you after each of these sentences.
1 Hitler was a General in the First World War.
2. Mussolini fought in the First World War.
3. The Fascists in Germany were called Nazis.
4. Italy and Germany had large armies in the 1930's.
5. The Fascists treated Jews badly.
6. Germany and Italy were crowded countries in the 1930's.
7. There were many German Jews living in Britain in the 1930's.
8. Mosley's Black shirts were nasty to many people.
9. Britain built a big army in the 1930's.
10. Jewish shops in London had their windows smashed in the 1930's.

Facts About World War II

Task: An exercise in chronology

Read these facts about the second world war. Carefully cut out each fact separately and paste them all in the correct chronological order on a separate piece of paper. As some of the facts have no date you will need to research in books to find the date of the events for those facts. Add carefully drawings of your own in the gaps provided to fit the facts.

The Allied armies land on the beaches of France June 1944.

March 1941 Hitler orders the invasion of Russia.

The battle of Britain is fought by the German and British airforces. Germans bomb London.

The first Atomic bomb is dropped on Japan in August 1945.

The Germans surrender. This is the end of the war in Europe.

The Japanese attack Pearl Harbour in June 1941. America says it is at war with Japan.

The German army is beaten in North Africa by the British army May 1942.

British forces invade Italy April 1943.

June 1933 Adolf Hitler is elected leader of Germany.

The German army invades Poland, Britain declares war on Germany.

City Children in a Wartime Village

EVIDENCE FROM SCHOOL LOG BOOKS FROM PILLING, BILSBOROUGH, AND WINMARLEIGH SCHOOLS LANCS

18th September 1939 School re-opened this morning, admitted 38 children evacuated from Salford. Miss Raybould a teacher came with them.

19th September 1939 Miss Raybould will spend the next three days inspecting the billets of the evacuees.

26th September 1939 Mr Pickup showed the children how to wear their gas masks.

1st October 1939 Mr Pickup visited school today to tell the children what to do in case of an air-raid.

12th December 1939 Nurse Kirkham paid a visit to inspect the heads of the evacuees for lice.

4th January 1940 The Church has given school the garden by the Church Room for gardening by the boys in the Dig For Victory Campaign.

12th April 1940 About 10 tons of scrap metal has been collected by the children and payment of £15 received for it. The money will be handed to the Ladies Knitting party to buy wool to knit goods for the troops.

27th September 1940 This week the teachers covered the windows of the large classroom with anti-splinter net.

12th May 1941 The school is open every day to collect money for War Weapons week. £2,188 taken this week.

4th February 1941 More evacuees have come from Salford. All evacuees are being taught in the Church hall by Salford teachers.

3rd March 1941 More furniture came from Salford for the Church hall.

2nd October 1941 The infants were taken today for a walk during the afternoon session to gather wild rose hips for the purpose of making jam (Vitamin C).

7th May 1942 Some of the older children were taken into the school garden to set potatoes.

6th October 1942 Salvage Week. The children have been allowed to pick scrap metal instead of having the usual Handiwork lessons.

"Now I want you to promise me you're all going to be really good little evacuees and not worry his Lordship."

Task: Selecting relevant facts

Cut out the pictures, stick them onto separate pieces of paper, and under each picture copy out parts of the Logbook which match each picture and its title.
Find out if there were evacuees in or from your area.

DIG FOR VICTORY

The Blackout

This stray pig was a Menace

Mr Worden of Lightfoot Lane was returning home after taking part in the entertainment at English Martyr's Hall when, as he was passing near the Cattle Market, the headlight of his car picked out a pig dashing about in the road. "A pig on its own on a main road is a danger, " said Mr Worden, "but in the blackout it's a menace, so I gave chase." After chasing up and down the street Mr Woden stopped to telephone the police for advice. "Corner the pig until we can send help" replied the police.
A big car coming in the opposite direction nearly killed the pig, and the driver of the car was not in the best of tempers after his car turned round in the road avoiding the beast. But the newcomer was ready to help and they cornered the pig. Mr Worden held onto the pig's ears whilst the stranger tied its legs with a cord to a lamp post. The beast still would not be still so Mr Worden sat on its back until the police arrived. "There I was with my dress suit on astride a porker. As a crowd had been attracted by the pig's squeals, I was glad of the blackout".

Street lights will not be lit.

At their meeting last night, Preston District Council decided not to test whether the lights could be seen from an aeroplane flying over the District. Councillor Maylie stated that the residents of the village had voted not to have their street lights switched on for the duration of the War and their wishes should be respected.

Fit proper blackout - Court Orders

John Smalley was said by the warden to have had only a very thin curtain for his window. He was fined 30shillings, and ordered to fit a proper blackout within 7 days. "In these serious times, the blackout rules must be more strictly obeyed, or penalties will be increased" said the magistrate today.

Task: Gathering information from newspapers

1. List 5 dangers to the public in the Blackout.
2. What had every householder to buy for their house in the Blackout ?
3. What did all motorists have to fit to their cars in the Blackout?
4. Why did the Government start the Blackout at the beginning of the war ?
5. Why was it important to know the time of the Moon's rising and setting in the Blackout ?

The Battle of Britain

Task: Gathering information from photographs

Imagine that you are the Editor of a Newspaper in 1940. It is the height of the Battle of Britain, when daily bombing raids were being carried out by the aeroplanes of the German Luftwaffe over Southern Britain. Write a Newspaper heading for each picture with the reporter's description of the scene below the heading in the space besides each picture.

Make a Model Anderton Air Raid Shelter

YOU WILL NEED.

A piece of corrugated cardboard 30cm by 30cm, a piece of stiff card 40cm by 40cm, an empty cereal box, pencil scissors, glue, paints, crayons or felt tips.

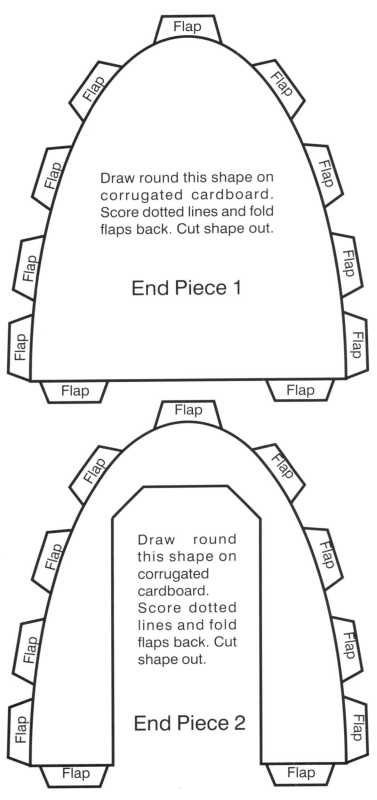

Flap

Draw round this shape on corrugated cardboard. Score dotted lines and fold flaps back. Cut shape out.

End Piece 1

Draw round this shape on corrugated cardboard. Score dotted lines and fold flaps back. Cut shape out.

End Piece 2

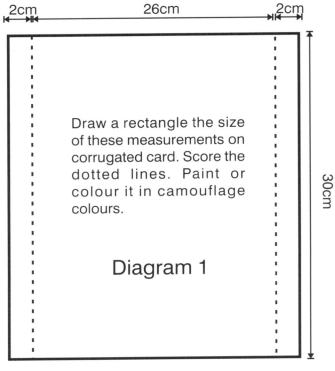

2cm   26cm   2cm

Draw a rectangle the size of these measurements on corrugated card. Score the dotted lines. Paint or colour it in camouflage colours.

Diagram 1

30cm

INSTRUCTIONS

Cut out a piece of corrugated cardboard the size of diagram.1.

Score along the dotted lines. Paint or colour the outside in camouflage colours. Let it dry properly. Draw round end pieces 1 & 2 on the corrugated card, colour them in camouflage, let dry well. Stick the flaps of your roof section curved around end piece 1. Glue this to your base card. Research what furniture or artefacts were kept in a shelter make them out of the cereal box and glue them inside your shelter. Glue end piece 2 to the roof piece and base card using the flaps. Add any trees, bushes or flowers made out of the cereal box to the base plate. Label your shelter carefully.

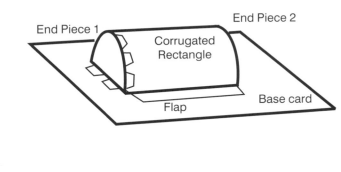

End Piece 1   Corrugated Rectangle   End Piece 2

Flap   Base card

Air Raids

Evidence from memories of the time

" I was 14 years old with three brothers and two sisters. We lived in a terraced house close to St Andrews dock, Hull, where the deep sea fishing trawlers docked. After several nights of being in the shelters because of heavy German bombing, the sirens went. Mam couldn't be bothered about going to the shelter so we went to shelter under our stairs which was the reinforced part of the house.

At that time we had a little dog and by some instinct it would go under the stairs before the sirens sounded. We all tucked into the little alcove waiting for the onslaught. Several bombs exploded nearby then there was a huge explosion and a rain of masonry, glass and clouds of black soot blacked everything out. When the dust had settled and all had quietened we wriggled out. We were astonished to look up and see the red of the sky where the bedrooms should have been. Mam checked us all one by one, no-one was hurt. We were all black as chimney sweeps. Our pet canary had been killed by the blast. Quickly Mam led us down to the shelter at the end of the street. I couldn't find my shoes so I went there barefoot.

As we entered in the candlelight a woman screamed seeing my face. She thought it was blood. She was only calmed when Mam washed my sooty face. Next day we were allowed back to salvage the few bits of furniture that had survived the blast. All our clothes had been blown to smithereens. We were rehoused nearby.

A few nights later we were rushed into the shelter as there was a big raid. When we came out next day there was a parachute bomb like a torpedo hanging from the telephone wires. Some navy men had defused it in the night. It was only a few nights later that our Harold was killed in an air raid that hit the Anderson shelter that he was in at his friend's house. His body was never found. After that tragedy, Mam moved us to the countryside near Barnsley out of the way of the bombing." Gladys Giles 1987.

Task: Asking, answering and selecting relevant information

Read the passage carefully, then write out ten questions for a friend in the class to answer about air raids. Here is one question to give you the idea.

Q1. Why do you think the Germans were bombing the town of Hull?

After your friend has answered the questions, give him/her a mark out of ten for selecting relevant facts.

Evidence from Letters

The Elms,
E. Malling,
Nr. Maidstone,
Kent.

May 12th 1942.

Dear Aunty

Thank you for writing me that letter. I asked my father whether he wore he helmet much and he said "no". Down here the hops are climbing the strings which you saw when we went for a walk. Not many days after you had gone a bomber, called a "Boston" crashed in the woods, unfortunately three men were killed and one suffering injuries in hospital. We heard two bombs explode which the plane was carting. I went up to see it, and

(PTO)

found a piece of glass which is made of a (very) strong substance, so that when a bullet hits it, it does not break through. I have made a ring out of it and am sending it to you. We are all getting on fine down here. I have a little garden of my own, and I grow my own crops on it, all the seeds that are left over from Daddys I have. with lots
of love from us all,
yours affectionately
Clifford

Some kisses for you all.

X Y X X C X W X Y

Mrs P. Halliwell
1 Windsor Avenue
Banworthaw
Nr Preston
Lancashire

Task: Reasoning Exercise

1. Why do you think Clifford's father didn't always wear his helmet ?
2. What sort of helmet do you think Clifford's father sometimes wore ?
3. Where do you think the Boston bomber was going with its load of bombs ?
4. What do you think caused the plane to crash in the wood in Kent ?
5. What part of the plane do you think the toughened glass came from ?
6. What do you think Clifford grew in his little garden ?
7. Why do you think Clifford made the pattern with his kisses?

Mapping the Changes in Europe 1939-45

Task: An exercise in chronology

School children from 1939-45 would follow the progress of the war on wall maps in their class. They would stick flag pins in the different countries as the two sides of the war advanced and retreated. Paste onto the correct place on the map of Europe the information about the major events of the war.

1 German Army invades Austria 1938

2 German armies take part of Czechoslovakia 1938.

3 Italy invades Albania 1939

4 Czechoslovakia invaded by Germany 1939

5 Germany invades Poland Sept.1939

6 Germany invades Denmark & Norway 1940

7 Holland and Belgium invaded by German army 1940

8 German army conquers Northern France 1940

9 France surrenders to Germans 1940

10 The German Army invades the Channel Isles 1940

11 Russia invades Latvia, Lithuania, and Estonia 1940

12 The battle of Britain fought over the skies of Southern England 1940

13 Rumania and Bulgaria join Germany and Italy in the war 1941.

14 1941 Germany invades Yugoslavia, Greece, and Crete

15 Germany declares war on Russia 1941

16 U.S.A. declares war on Germany. Heavy bombing of Germany 1941

17 American and British forces invade Sicily and Italy 1943

18 Russian army pushes German army out of Russia. 1943

19 The Allied armies land in France on "D" day June 1944

20 Russian troops capture Rumania and Bulgaria 1944

21 The German army surrenders in Italy 1945

22 The Russian Armies free Poland, Hungary, and Czechoslovakia 1945

23 British, American and Russian armies meet up in Berlin

Mapping the Changes in Europe 1939-45

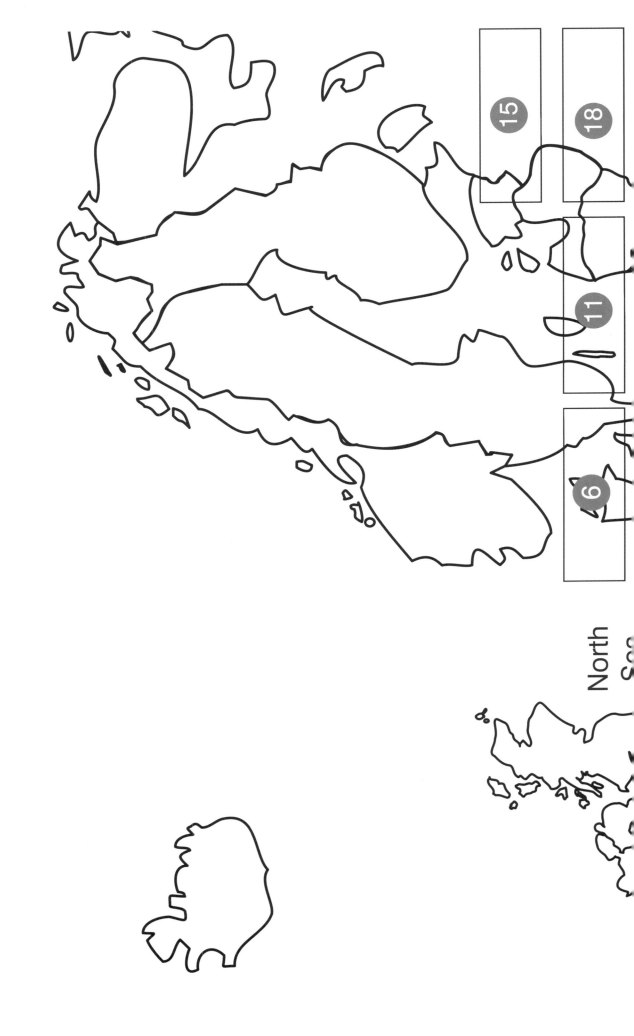

North

See

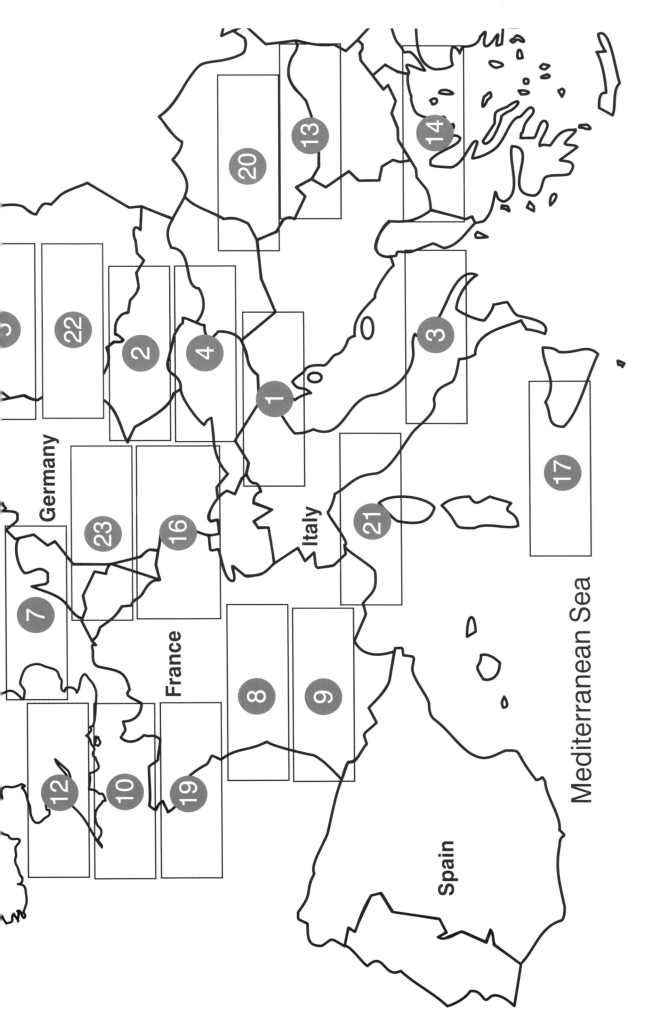

The Progress of the War 1939-45

Germany

France

Italy

Spain

Mediterranean Sea

All Change for Women in World War II

From Housewife to Land Army Girl.

"My Alfred was called up straight away as he was a reserve Navy engineer. He didn't want me in London with all the bombing so he persuaded me to join the Land army. I loved it because I'd been brought up in the country. I was on farms in Norfolk. I didn't have any worries about rations, there was lots of fresh food! I worried about my Alfred though, lots of escort ships sunk on his Atlantic convoy runs. When the war ended I persuaded Alfred to get a mechanics job in the village.I still help out with bits on the farms."

1) Why do you think her husband didn't want her in London in the wartime ?
2) Why do you think she didn't have any worries about wartime rationing ?

From School Leaver to Parachute Maker

"Well I was just 14 in 1939. I was going to work at the Co-op as a seamstress as I was good at sewing. Then they were short of good machinists at the parachute making works, it was good pay but long hours. By the end of the war I was in charge of my section, then I got to be in charge at Burtons Tailors alteration department. It was there I met my husband, got married, and then I was housewife and mother soon."

1) Why did she get a job as a seamstress ?
2) Why do you think the parachute makers worked long hours ?

From Cotton Weaver to Bomb Maker.

"Straight from school in 1936 I started as a weaver. It was good and I enjoyed the company. Then with the war they came round asking for volunteers to work at the Munitions work. They wanted us weavers as we had nimble fingers, just right for filling bombs with explosives. I went. I thought I was doing my bit for the war effort. It was awful at first, shift work, sometimes working all night, sometimes till 10 at night and then the train home. And the explosions, 3 of my pals lost their fingers when powder exploded. Bombs I made blew up them dams in Germany though, and lots more besides. When war was over I was a G.I. bride. I married Ike who I'd met at a Dance in Wigan. I sailed to America with lots more girls on the Queen Elizabeth and then I was a Housewife in Boston U.S.A."

1) Why were weavers picked to do munitions work?
2) Give 2 reasons why she didn't like munitions work.

All Change for Women in World War II

From Housewife to Aircraft Maker

"When my Fred signed up for the Army, I felt lost, and then he was sent to France. He was in the battle at Dunkirk. His company held the line whilst the rest got back to England. After a few months the Red Cross told me he was a prisoner of war. I was lost and so sad. My friend told me I needed to get out of the house. So I signed up on a training scheme. I became a fitter and made wings for Halifax bombers. I felt I was doing something for the war, and the friendship of other women in our factory was grand. When my Fred came back in 1945 he was nothing but skin and bone, so I went back to being a housewife."

1) Why did her friend tell her to get out of the house, after her husband was taken prisoner?
2) Why do you think she went back to being a housewife after the war ?

On Reflection...

JOIN THE **WAAF**

From Shop Girl to Army Chauffeur

"There I was fed up and bored working as bagger in a Grocers with a miserably mean boss. Well the war was just what I wanted, a chance to escape. So I signed up in the W.R.A.C. I volunteered for the driver's course and spent the rest of the war as chauffeur on H.Q.staff, driving the high and mighty officers around England. I loved it. Many of them were real sweeties! I met so many people, had such fun with the other girls in our car pool, and met my George the chief mechanic who kept our vehicles running. Now him and me have our own Garage business. He mends the cars and I serve the petrol and keep the customers happy!"

1) Why do you think she was pleased when war broke out?
2) Why do you think she chose to run a garage after the war?

From Farm Girl to Radar Control Room Operator.

"My dad wanted me to work on the farm as soon as I left school at 14. I didn't want to but I had to, so when the war started I signed up for the Women's Auxiliary Air Force. I told a lie that I was an office girl or else they would have kept me down on the farm with my grumpy Dad. I was trained as a Radar operator and worked in the control room at fighter H.Q. I met lots of dashing young pilots, fell in love and married one. But then the great sadness. He was killed in action over Germany on bomber escort in 1944. After the war I got a job at Gatwick, met another pilot and married again."

1) Why do you think she didn't like the farm?
2) Why did she meet so many pilots ?

Task: Evidence from oral interviews

1. Answer the questions found at the end of each oral interview.
2. List as many changes for women in the war that you can find.
3. Research the type of jobs women do nowadays.

Posters that Helped Win the War

Task:

For each poster write out:-
1) Who you think the poster was aimed at ?
2) What you think the poster was trying to get that person to do ?
Finally, design your own poster to encourage people to 'Dig for Victory'.

Food in the 1940's
Each person's ration for a week.

| About 2 or 3 ounces of meat (50-75grams) | 1 ounce of cheese (25 grams) | 4 ounces of bacon or ham (100 grams) | 1 or 2 eggs |

2 ounces of tea (50 grams) 8 ounces of sugar (200 grams) 8 ounces of butter or fat (200 grams)

Food not on the ration

Fruit
Only fruit grown in this country was in the shops, and only available when ripe.

Vegetables
There were often shortages of vegetables. Often they were only available for a short time.

Milk
Supplies of milk to cities were often stopped by air raids on railways.

Dig for victory food from spare land.
People were encouraged to dig up their gardens, yards or any spare land to grow fruit and vegetables for themselves. People who could do this would add a lot to their family's diet. If they had enough room they often kept a few hens for their eggs and meat.

Task: Finding out about aspects of the period
On three large circles of paper draw the food for a Breakfast, Lunch and Tea that a child living in 1941 might have enjoyed. Be careful that you do not use a person's total ration in one day. Compare this diet to your own for one day.

Evidence from Advertisements

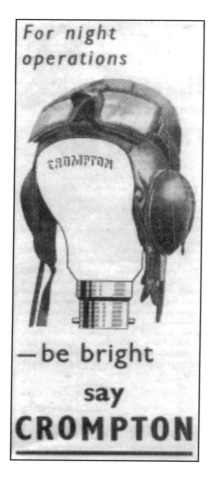

The National Health Service

Facts about health before 1948

- Every one had to pay for each visit to the Doctor.
- If you had to go into hospital you had to pay for everything.
- If you could not afford the expensive treatment in one go, then you had to pay the Doctor so much each week. He had a man who came round to collect your money each week.
- Children and babies who needed a vaccination against common but often fatal illnesses such as diphtheria, smallpox and tuberculosis had to pay for every injection.
- If you needed spectacles or treatment for your teeth you had to pay for each visit and all your treatment.

Effects on people's health before 1948

- People avoided going to the Doctor until they were really ill.
- Poor people were sometimes very ill before they went to the doctor, often so ill that they died.
- People tried to cure themselves using herbs and spices and cheap medicines.
- Many children were not vaccinated and died of smallpox, diphtheria, and tuberculosis.
- Many people had very bad teeth or not many teeth in their mouths.

People queuing at a large town's free Hospital in the 1930s.

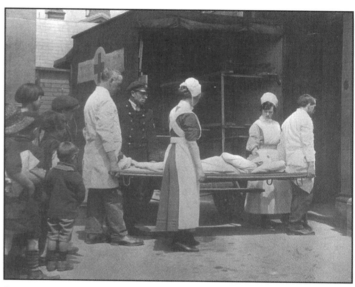

Poor children watch as a patient is brought to hospital by ambulance. Only richer people could afford an ambulance.

The National Health Service 1948 brought everyone

- Free Medical advice from doctors, dentists and opticians.
- Free Medical prescriptions.
- Free Spectacles.
- Free Hospital Treatment.
- Free Immunisation and vaccination.
- Free Hearing Aids.
- All false teeth and dental treatment free.

Effects of the National Health Service 1948-51

- 187 million prescriptions written by doctors.
- 1938 - 65,000 cases of diphtheria.
  1953 - 53 cases of diphtheria.
- 12 million pairs of glasses issued.
- 151,000 hearing aids issued
- 14 million pairs of false teeth issued
- Hospital admissions doubled.

Task: Can you link the causes and effects of changes in Britain's health?

1. Why did many people avoid visiting their doctor before 1948?.
2. Why did some people make their own medicines before 1948?
3. Why did doctors have money collectors before 1948?
4. What caused many children to die of diphtheria before 1948?
5. Why did 12 million people get glasses after 1948?
6. Why were there double the number of Hospital admissions after 1948?
7. List 7 reasons why poor people welcomed the National Health service in 1948.

On the Road 1930 to 1950

Many routes to the seaside had long queues on summer weekends. The roads were narrow, with many bends and hold ups through tiny villages, or busy towns.

Motor vehicle numbers:-

1930	1,505,000
1950	3,290,000
1970	12,871,000
1990	24,209,000

Unemployed men were given work in the 1930s making new dual carriage roads to by-pass many towns or villages. These were called arterial roads and had separate footpaths and cycleways alongside the road.

The increase of lorries carrying goods, in place of the railways, meant that roads built for only light traffic had to carry heavy traffic. This picture shows one of the main routes from industrial Lancashire to the towns of Yorkshire.

Many special cheaper family cars were produced in the 1930s. The Austin 7, the Morris 8 and the Ford Popular were all made with small engines and simple family comforts to bring motoring to the ordinary people.

On the Road 1950 to 1990

The first motorway (M6) was opened in December 1958. It bypassed Preston in Lancashire, which had serious traffic jams. It was a great success. Many other motorways followed freeing many towns from traffic jams.

By the 1990s many motorways had become scenes of daily traffic jams, many miles long. Motorists and lorry drivers have become used to long waits especially near cities and busy motorway intersections.

The Suez crisis in the 1950s meant that petrol became scarce and expensive. Many firms produced small cars that would carry a family but travel along way on a Gallon of petrol.
This is a Bond Minicar.

The Morris Minor, the Ford Anglia and the Austin Mini, were all cars produced from 1960 which sought to give cheap family motoring to as many people as possible.

Task: Listing Change & Continuity

Look carefully at the text and pictures on pages 40 and 41 then list:-
1. 10 things that have changed on the roads from 1930 to 1990.
2. 10 things that have stayed the same from 1930 to 1990.

Holidays
1930 to 1975

Holidays
1930 to 1975

Task: Compare and Contrast

1. Cut out the cards and messages and paste the matching cards and messages together on three separate pieces of paper. Make an educated guess of the date of each holiday. Write down the date and the reasons for your guess. Discuss this with your teacher.

2. Compare the 3 holidays and state which holiday you think gives the best value for a family of four.

3. State which holiday you would choose to go on and give the reasons for your choice.

Postcard 1

POST CARD

The man took our picture as we watched the Pierrot show on the pier. Our digs are clean and Mrs Briggs makes our food up nice. We have been on the Big Dipper, The Ghost Train and Noah's Ark on the Pleasure Beach. Our Bert has been paddling and sandcastle making every day. Our Dad reckons he'll wear the donkeys out.

Regards Mavis

Mrs Davies,
72, Balmoral Avenue,
Headingley,
Leeds
Yorkshire.

Postcard 2

It's 90° in the shade here. Our apartment's lovely, it's got it's own pool. We can have a slap-up meal at night for a fiver each! And beer's only 20pence a bottle. The disco goes on till 2a.m. and even then it's still warm outside. Dad has tried squid he says it's rubbery. But you can still get chips and fish.

love Lynne and family.

Mr & Mrs Black,
102 Park Road,
Islington,
LONDON
N1 3TF
ENGLAND

Postcard 3

POST CARD

It's marvellous here at Pontin's, something to do all day long. Our Joanne joins the other children at swimming, crazy golf and concerts. Dad enjoys the darts and bowls and evening concerts, and I eventually got him to dance in the ballroom. They feed us all 5000 quick and good. Dad wants to book for next year.

love Alice.

Mr & Mrs Whitehead,
96 Wolverhampton Road,
Walsall,
Staffs.

Change in the Kitchen 1930 to 1990
A Typical Kitchen in a Terraced House

1930's

Cooking was still carried out on the fire range, there was only a cold water supply to the sink. Meat, butter and cheese were kept in a cool meat safe. Washing was done in the dolly tub, and wrung dry in the mangle.

1950's

Cooking was by electric cooker, the sink had a hot water supply. Food was still stored in the meat safe. An electric washer was moved next to the sink to wash clothes which were wrung out by an electric mangle.

1970's

An automatic washer spins and dries the clothes, the sink is a stainless steel unit with mixer taps. The cooker has an automatic oven timer and overhead grill. Fresh food is kept in the refrigerator.

1990's

The kitchen is fully fitted with wipe down surfaces. There is a dishwasher, separate cooking hob, eye level oven, microwave oven, fridge/freezer, automatic washer and tumble drier to get clothes perfectly dry. The sink has a waste disposal unit.

Task: Gathering information from various sources.

Using examples from the decades shown above list the following:-
1. The source of power and equipment used for cooking.
2. The equipment used for keeping food cool and fresh.
3. The equipment used for washing and drying clothes.
4. The equipment used for drying pots and pans.
5. Look carefully at the evidence and your answers then put the kitchens in order of safest and most hygienic, giving reasons for your choice.

Change in the Living Room 1930 to 1990
A Typical Living Room in a Suburban Semi-detached House

1930's

The main source of heating was the coal fire. The main items of furniture were made of wood. The wireless and the wind up gramophone provided the families leisure entertainment along with songs around the piano.

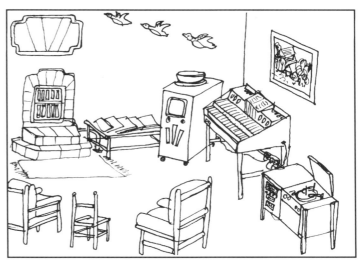

1950's

The heat is provided by a gas fire. The table and chairs have metal frames. The television has a large magnifying screen to enlarge the picture. The radiogram can play 10 records one after another. The electric organ can imitate 9 instruments.

1970's

The room is heated by oil fired central heating. The Hi-Fi has a tape deck as well as a 3 band radio and record deck. The T.V. receives 4 channels, and the Keyboard will give you the sounds of anything from a pop group to a full orchestra. The children have a game that lets them shoot at targets on their T.V.

1990's

The gas fired central heating is backed up by the coal effect gas fire. The double glazed windows help keep the room warm and the traffic noise out. The furniture has fireproof filling inside real leather. The T.V. can receive 54 channels thanks to the satellite dish. The family regularly record programmes or watch films through their Video recorder. The whole family enjoy fact recall, games and connecting with many countries through their Internet C.D. ROM P.C

Task: Selecting relevant information.

From the pictures and text list ten ways in which Technology has changed Living rooms from 1930 to 1990.

Britain's Youth Set Rocking

Bill Haley Brings Wild African Rock Beat to London's Teenagers.

With his "Kiss Curl" and his wild guitar rhythms, Bill Haley and his band had Teddy Boys and Girls rocking and "Jiving" in the aisles of the Hammersmith Palace last night. The American groups beat music had echoes of the African Jungle drums.

Elvis "The Pelvis" Rocks Teenagers Into Frenzy with his Wiggle

The latest American "Rock" star Elvis Presley is shocking parents in America with his "wiggling" hip movements as he sings his latest popular song "Jail House Rock". Many parents feel their daughters will be lead into evil by the wiggle of the Pop Stars Hips. Presley's records have twice hit the top of the 'Pop Charts'

Long Haired Liverpool Lads send Young Girl Fans into a Screaming Frenzy

Four young long haired Liverpudlians in collarless suits called the Beatles are about to take the "Pop" scene by storm. Playing in a cellar club called "The Cavern," to packed audiences of wildly screaming teenage girls, they belt out catchy songs written by two of the group. Their first release looks set to storm to No.1 in the "Pop Charts" March 22nd 1963.

Task: Evidence from Newspapers.

1. What instrument do you think gave Bill Haley's music its Rhythm?
2. Where do you think Bill Haley came from ?
3. What did the reporter think Bill Haley's Music sounded like ?
4. Why do you think some Americans were shocked by Elvis Presley ?
5. What do you think was Elvis Presley's nickname ?
6. What was the title of one of Elvis Presley's records ?
7. What does the report tell you about the Beatles appearance ?
8. Who do you think went to the "Cavern" to watch the Beatles?
9. Who do you think wrote the Beatles songs ?
10. Write your own Newspaper report about your favourite Popstar.

Sport for All 1930 to 1980

47,000 Watch Hutton Beat Bradman's Batting Record at the Oval

The cloth caps were thrown high in the sky today as Yorkshire's Len Hutton snatched the World Batting Record for England against the might of Australia's bowling here at the Oval today. It is estimated that 500,000 more people listened to the event broadcast on the wireless. (1938)

Matthew's Magic Wins the F.A.Cup for Blackpool in Lancashire Derby at Wembley in Front of 100,000.

Wizard of dribble Stanley Matthew's laid on the magic passes as Blackpool came back to win by 4-3 against neighbours Bolton. Wembley was a sea of Tangerine as the people of Blackpool celebrated. The Game was watched by over 8 million people on T.V. (1953)

Bannister Breaks the 4 Minute Barrier for the Mile at Oxford University Track.

There were only a handful of spectators to see Roger Bannister, paced by 6 other runners, smash the 4 minute mile barrier. Over 12 million people were able to witness the trainee doctor's run as the T.V. news, and film crews brought the event into British homes and cinemas. (1954)

London Marathon Captivates the Capitol

Close on half a million spectators lined the streets of London today in bright sunshine to cheer on the 30,000 runners in the London Marathon. Many runners were in fancy dress and all were hoping to raise money for charity. T.V. carried the event to 40 million homes throughout Europe. (1980)

Task: Interpreting the evidence.

1. Divide a plain piece of paper into 3 columns, put the headings:-
   People taking part.
   People watching at the event.
   T.V. or Radio audience.
   Enter the correct figures for each event in the separate columns. Study these facts and then put the events in order of largest to smallest audience for the event.

Fashion 1930 to 1980

1930's Women

Short skirts.
Shaped hemlines.
Bobbed hair
Lip stick, make up.
Close fitting hats.
Flesh coloured silk stockings.
Slacks.
Daring swimsuits.

1930's Men

Baggy Trousers.
Sport's Jackets.
Wide Jacket lapels.
Flat hats.
Brogue shoes.
Striped ties.
Coloured shirts.
Belted raincoats.
All in one swimwear.

1940's Women

Uniforms.
Pinafores.
Headscarves.
Permed wavy hair.
Nylons.
Post war longer flared skirts.
Jackets with wide lapels.
Narrow waists and flared hip lines.

1940's men

Uniforms.
Demob blue Serge suits.
Flashy ties.
Trilbys.
Double breasted jackets.
Shetland sleeveless pullovers.

1950's women

Flared skirts.
Tight fitting sweaters.
Longer hem lines.
Bikini Swimsuits.
Tight waisted suits.
Stilletto high heels.
"Bobby" short socks.
"Can-Can" underskirts.

1950's men

"Drain pipe" tight trousers.
Thick crepe soled shoes.
Bootlace ties.
Long "Teddy-Boy" bright coloured jackets.
Long greased hair and "Sideburns".

1960's Women

Mini skirts.
P.V.C. Knee length boots.
Bobbed hairstyles.
Straight tight shift dresses.
Bright contrasting colours.
P.V.C. Macs.
Winkle picker shoes.

1960's Men

Longer hair.
Winkle picker shoes.
Collarless suits.
Sweaters.
Anaracks.
Bright "Kipper" ties.
Button down shirt collars.

1970's Women

Ankle length skirts and dresses.
Long hair.
Thigh length boots.
Platform shoes.
Flower and Psychedelic patterns in bright colours.
Flared trousers.
Trainers.

1970's Men

Long hair.
Moustaches.
Beards.
Flared trousers.
Platform shoes.
Ankle length coats.
Flower and Psychedelic patterns in bright colours.
Trainers.

Task: Communicating information in a variety of ways.

Choose a decade and make a poster to advertise Men's or Women's Fashion for that decade.

Events in the History of Flying 1930 to 1990

The airship R101 with 24 crew and 30 passengers in a luxury cabin beneath the gas filled balloon frame was forced down in a freak storm in France on its test flight to Paris in 1930. Only 6 people survived. In the 1930's a German airship crossed the Atlantic weekly with 40 crew and 20 passengers in 56 hours. The airship Hindenburg exploded on its mooring rig in New York in 1937 killing everyone on board. This put a stop to Airship flights.

From 1939 to 1945 war meant many advances in flying. A Jet powered plane developed in 1945 by Sir Frank Whittle led to much faster flight and the breaking of the sound barrier in 1949 at 1,200 k.p.h. The Helicopter, with vertical lift off and the ability to land in small spaces was built for troop carrying in the war.

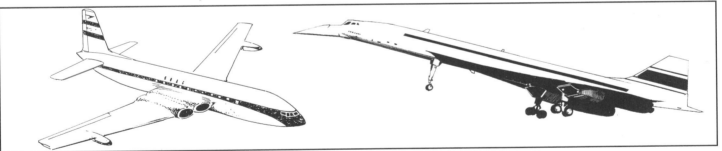

• In the 1950s the Comet airliner flew across the Atlantic in a matter of 9 hours carrying over 150 passengers in comfort. In 1955 Comet III flew 30,000 miles around the world in under 67 hours. A daily Jet flight link to America was established in 1953.
• Concord a supersonic Jet passenger aeroplane had its first passenger crossing of the Atlantic in 1972. It could carry over 120 passengers to America in under 4 hours. By the 1990's American built Boeing "Jumbo Jets" could carry up to 500 people at high speeds over long distances.

Task: Picking out the highlights.

1. Give 2 reasons why airships stopped flying after 1937.
2. What improvement in speed did jet planes bring to the Atlantic crossing in the 1950's.
3. List 2 advances in flying brought about by the 2nd World War.
4. List the differences between Concorde and a Boeing Jumbo jet.
5. What changes did Concorde bring to Atlantic passenger flight ?
6. Why was a Helicopter very useful in wartime ?
7. Research in books to find and draw Fighter planes of 1939-45.

Immigration to Britain 1950 to 1970

Erroll Barrett's story

"I was brought up in Barbados in the sunny Caribbean. My teacher came from England, she was always telling us about the "Mother country" where there were lots of jobs. When I passed my exams I couldn't get a job in Barbados. My cousin Clyde wrote telling me about how much he earned as a London Underground station worker.

I borrowed my fare for the boat journey from my Dad. At first I hated the dirty airless Underground but I worked hard and long hours. Now I'm Station Master and live in a better part of Balham. My wife works in the ticket office, and we have sent our 2 children back to Barbados for their schooling. Schools there give a better education to black children than London schools."

Vijay Singh's story

"My father left Pakistan in 1947 with our family because he was afraid of the hatred for Hindus in the newly formed country. He took us to Uganda in Africa, a British colony. He set up a village store to supply the English farmers and their African workers with everything they needed. He always kept his British passport and brought us up to speak just English and his native Gujerati. When General Amin became leader of Uganda my father saw trouble coming. He moved us out. As we drove to the airport the Africans were throwing bricks through the cab window.

Father took us to a friend from his village in Pakistan who had a shop in Birmingham. We lived in one room above their shop until father found a corner shop in Walsall. Now we are open 8 till late. We all work in the shop. We sell everything and are doing well. My father worries about people who are abusive about our colour and jealous of our successful shop."

Samina Patel's story

"I was sent for from a village near Bombay when I was 16. My father had arranged a marriage for me to Mustak who was from our village. He had worked in a weaving mill in Bradford for 3 years. He was clever and saw bad times coming for the mills in the woollen trade, so he opened a take away selling Curries to people. Most of our trade was late at night with people buying a meal after a night out. We now have a restaurant in the town centre and we employ 12 people. My son is training to be an Accountant and my daughter is a Doctor."

Task: Cause and effect.

1 Why do you think Erroll Barrett came to England?
2 How did Erroll Barrett feel when he first came to England?
3 Why did Erroll Barrett quickly become Station Master?
4 Why did Mr.Barrett send his children to school in Barbados?
5 What do you think caused Mr. Singh to leave Pakistan?
6 Why do you think Mr. Singh left Uganda?
7 What do you think upsets Mr.Singh most about life in England?
8 What do you think caused Samina's husband to open a take away?
9 What time of day was the busiest time for the Singh's take away?
10 Find out about what caused different people from outside your area to move into your area.

Emigration from Britain 1950 t0 1990

Mock 1950 advertisement.

A home and a job in the Sun. £10 gets you to Australia Land of Sun, Sea and Sand. A home and a job in the land of the future.

Family men with a trade or skill in the building industry given priority. £10 gives you your voyage out per person, a place in rented housing and help with finding a job. Australian wages are twice as good as British poor pay. Apply to Australia House, Trafalgar Square, London for your assisted fare to Australia.

Be your own boss and earn your family a place in the sunshine.

NO RATIONS OR RESTRICTIONS, LAND AND HOMES FOR ALL.

Mock 1985 advertisement.

Earn your worth in the land of the Free. Skilled Medical Professionals wanted in the Sunshine States of the U.S.A.

Come over and join us!

Get away from dull days and a cramped life style to the wide open spaces of the sunny lands of Florida. Treble your pay & work with the latest equipment.

A luxury home with your own swimming pool in acres of land comes free with the contract for all doctors and surgeons. Contact the Florida State Medical Recruitment Board, U.S.A.Embassy, Grosvenor Square, London for details. Please enclose career details.

Task: Using evidence.

1. List 7 reasons why people might want to emigrate to Australia from Britain in 1950.
2. List 6 reasons why a doctor might want to emigrate to Florida in 1985.
3. List the reasons you think made people want to start a new life in a different country.
4. Why do you think the Australians and Americans wanted people from Britain to emigrate to their countries?

Date the Artefact

A game for 2 to 4 players, + 1 referee.

INSTRUCTIONS

Cut out these pictures of objects from the 1930's to the 1990's to make a set of 30 cards. Make yourselves 3 date labels with 1930 to 1950 ; 1950 to 1970 ; and 1970 to present on them. Turn the object cards upside down. Each player picks up a card in turn and puts it under the date label he or she thinks it fits. The referee then asks 'Are there any challenges?'. If the other players think the date is wrong they may challenge the players decision, and win the card for themselves if they choose the correct date. The referee awards the card for each correct answer and the card is removed from play. The winner is the player with the most cards.

Date the Artefact

Answers for referee.

The Exploration of Space 1926 to 1997

The Russian Lunar 2 spacecraft crash lands on the Moon 1959.

1989 the American spacecraft Voyager 2 flies past Venus.

1976 two U.S.A Viking spacecraft visit Mars, but find no sign of life.

The first spacewoman Valentina Tereshkova (U.S.S.R.) orbits the earth 1963.

In 1987 a Russian cosmonaut spent 326 days in space.

Russian Alexi Leonov makes the first Space walk for 20 minutes in 1965.

1957 Sputnik 1a Russian satellite is the first object in space.

1983 the European and American Spacelab is launched to provide a permanent workplace in space.

Yuri Gargarin(U.S.S.R.) the first human to orbit the earth in 1961.

1996 A piece of meteorite from Mars is thought to have signs of life.

Neil Armstrong(U.S.A.) walks on the Moon 1969.

U.S.A Robert Goddard builds the world's first liquid fuelled rocket 1926.

1943 The German V2 rocket powered bombs launched on Britain from Northern France.

Vostock rocket U.S.S.R. sends Gagarin into orbit 1961.

Mercury/Atlas rocket sends John Glenn into orbit 1962.

1968 U.S.A. Saturn rocket powers Apollo Moon explorations.

1981 European countries Rocket "Ariane" launches satellites.

1981.U.S.A. Shuttle space craft which can be re-used is first launched.

1984 Chinese "Long March III" launches Chinese satellite.

1987 Russian Energya rocket launches Buran space shuttle.

Mariner 10(U.S.A.) sends back pictures of Mercury 1975.

1975 U.S.A's Apollo and U.S.S.R's Souz spacecraft meet up in space.

John Glenn(U.S.A.) 1962 orbits the earth 3 times.

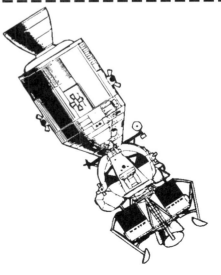

Task: An exercise in chronology.

1   Down the centre of a large piece of paper, vertically set out a time line from 1926 to 1997, marking on the line every five years. Cut out the Space Exploration Facts and paste them as near to their correct date as possible. Use research to illustrate your work.

Britons Give for Famine Relief 1980's

Pop Stars and T.V. Comics make Britons give millions for African Famine Relief.

A Popstar changes lives for millions in Africa and the world.

Bob Geldof saw T.V. pictures of children and adults starving to death in Ethiopia and Somalia in 1984. He was very upset by the pictures of suffering and death. He persuaded other Pop stars and groups to make a record "Do they know its Christmas ?" The musicians all gave their services free of charge. The record made millions of pounds. Not satisfied with this, Geldof then organised two simultaneous "Pop" concerts in Britain and America.

Many thousands paid to go to the concerts. Television pictures of the concerts were sold all over the world. Over 40 million pounds were raised to save people in Africa from Famine.

Comic Lenny Henry raises laughter and Millions of pounds for African and British children.

In 1989 Lenny Henry saw children starving in Africa on T.V. He watched a news items about children in need in Britain. He made other funny people give their comedy free on T.V. Lenny Henry got millions to buy a plastic RED NOSE and wear it on "RED NOSE DAY". People took part in funny events for sponsor money Millions watched "COMIC RELIEF" night on T.V. Over 17 million pounds was raised in 1988 and 27 million pounds in 1989 to help others.

Task: Finding reasons for peoples actions.

1. What do you think upset Bob Geldof?
2. Why do you think Bob Geldof put on a Pop Concert?
3. What do you think made people all over the world watch the Band Aid concert?
4. Why do you think Bob Geldof called his concert "Live Aid"?
5. What made Lenny Henry want to hold a "Comic Relief" programme?
6. Why did Lenny Henry want Comics to give their comedy free?
7. Why do you think Lenny Henry wanted everyone to wear a "Red Nose" on "Comic Relief Day"?
8. Why do you think Lenny Henry called it all "Comic Relief Day"?
9. What other things do you think helped raise the £17 million on "Comic Relief Day"?
10. Make up your own "Comic Relief" sponsored event and Jokes.

Radio, T.V. and the Cinema Since 1930

Families would enjoy music, plays and news on the radio in 1930.

"Disc Jockeys" since 1950 have made music very popular.

Very few people could watch the first T.V. programmes in 1936.

"Snow White" by Walt Disney was the first colour film in 1938.

28 million people each week went to the cinema in 1948.

Satellites brought the first T.V. pictures from America in 1961.

1) In 1930, families would enjoy _____, _____ and _____ on their _____.

2) Since 1950 _____ _____ have made _____ very popular.

3) Very few people could _____ the first _____ programme in 1936.

4) The first colour _____ in 1938 was called _____ _____ .

5) In 1948 28 _____ people each week went to the _____.

6) The first T.V. pictures from _____ came by _____ in 1961.

7) Carefully draw and colour your own picture of "Snow White and the Seven Dwarfs".

Level 2

Radio, T.V. and the Cinema Since 1930

The B.B.C. started broadcasting in 1927. Families would sit around their wireless set and enjoy music, comedy, plays and news items in their own homes. Radio linked men away at the war with their families. From the 1950's people would listen to the many "pop" music programmes on their transistor radios wherever they were.

In 1936 the first T.V. broadcasts started, but few people could watch as the broadcasts only reached the London area. The Coronation of Queen Elizabeth II in 1953 made T.V. more popular. In 1961 the first live pictures were sent by satellite from America. Colour T.V. programmes came to Britain in 1967.

Many people went to the cinema every week when talking and coloured films were introduced in the 1930's. Most large British towns had more than 10 cinemas. By 1948 twenty eight million visits were made to the cinema in Britain. In the 1960's when most people had a T.V. many of the cinemas closed down.

1) When did people start listening to the "wireless"?
2) When was the first T.V. Broadcast ?
3) Where did the first satellite pictures come from ?
4) What special event was on T.V. in 1953 ?
5) What sort of films did people watch in the 1930's ?
6) How many people visited the cinema in one week in 1948 ?
7) What caused many cinemas to close down in the 1960's.

1) Why did only a few people watch T.V. in 1936 ?
2) Why was the radio important in the war ?

Carefully draw and colour your own picture of a 1930's family listening to their wireless set.

Level 3

Radio, T.V. and the Cinema Since 1930

The B.B.C. started television broadcasting in the London area in 1936, but stopped for the war. More transmitting stations built for the T.V. screening of the coronation of Queen Elizabeth II in 1953 led many people to people have their own T.V. In 1961 live pictures were beamed by satellite from America. In 1967 colour T.V. was available in Britain. In the 1980's video recorders meant films and other T.V. programmes could be viewed anytime.

Films with the actors talking in them led to a rapid growth in cinemas in the 1930's. Colour films followed in the late 1930's. New cinemas had exotic styles and luxury fittings. Many towns had 10 or more cinemas. By 1948 twenty eight million cinema visits were made to cinemas in one week. The popularity of television in the 1960's led to the closure of many cinemas. By 1968 there were only 3 million cinema visits per week.

The first Radio programmes started in 1927. Families gathered round their "wireless" sets to enjoy music, plays, comedies and news. In the war radio kept families in touch with the troops serving abroad. The transistor developed in the 1960's led to easily portable radios. From 1950 "Disc Jockeys" playing "pop" music to large audiences created a new musical industry.

A 1) When were the first radio programmes started ?
2) What service did the radio do in the war ?
3) How did the coronation in 1953 affect television?
4) Why did satellites improve television viewing ?
5) Which type of film made more people go to the cinema ?
6) How many more people went to the cinema every week in 1948 than 1968 ?
7) What effect did the invention of video recorders have on T.V. ?

B 1) What evidence suggests a lot of people wanted to watch Elizabeth II's coronation ?
2) Why was the radio important in the war ?
3) Why do you think lots of cinemas were built in the 1930's ?
4) Why do you think "Disc Jockeys" helped develop the record music industry ?
5) Why do you think more people watched T.V. than visited the cinema in the 1960's ?

C Carefully draw and colour your own picture of a family in 1953 watching the Coronation of Queen Elizabeth II on T.V.

Level 4

Radio, T.V. and the Cinema Since 1930

The B.B.C., founded in 1927, brought music, comedy, plays and speedy News coverage on the "wireless" to most homes in Britain in the 1930's. The Forces radio linked the troops, and their families and played an important role in keeping up the nation's morale through the war. The development of the valveless transistor radio in the 1960's meant that tiny portable radios could be carried everywhere. Commercial radio using V.H.F. waves led to local and commercial radio stations so that by the 1990's everyone had a choice of a wide range of programmes. "Disc Jockeys" playing "pop" music on the radio have led to a new musical industry since the 1950's.

The World's first television service provided by the B.B.C. opened in 1936. The transmitters were only effective for a 30 mile radius so only Londoners could receive the pictures. The station closed for the war. More transmitters meant that almost all of Britain could watch the Coronation of Queen Elizabeth II in 1953 in black and white, even if it meant crowding into the one house in the street that had a set.

This event's success led to an increase in the numbers of people having T.V. sets. Commercial T.V. started broadcasting in 1955 with more varied viewing. From 1961 space satellites meant that events from all around the world could be broadcast as they happened. Colour T.V. programmes were available to British viewers from 1967. The invention of the Video recorder has meant that films can be watched in your own home, and T.V programmes can be viewed at a later date.

The development of Satellite broadcasting to individual homes has brought large dish shaped aerials, greater competition and variety to viewing. The prospect of shopping by T.V. common in the U.S.A. and Europe is still to be expanded in Britain.

In 1927 "The Jazz Singer" was the first film to have the actors talking in it, and marked the huge advance in Cinema expansion in the 1930's. Colour was first introduced in Walt Disney's cartoon feature "Snow White" in 1938. New cinemas with exotic styles and luxury fittings were built in many town centres. The "double bill" of film and live entertainment drew thousands to a regular weekly attendance. Smaller picture houses in different areas meant that most medium sized British towns had over 10 cinemas. The smaller cinemas changed their "bill" twice or three times per week. By 1948 twenty eight million visits were made to cinemas in one week in Britain. By 1968 this figure was down to 3 million, due to television. Cinemas were converted to "bingo" halls or night clubs. The late 1980's saw the growth of multi-screened cinemas on the edge of towns which have brought films back in popularity.

1) Why was the Forces Radio important in the Second World War?
2) How did the Transistor affect radio listening?
3) Which industry expanded because of the "Disc Jockey's" job?
4) Why were there not so many T.V.sets in 1936?
5) How did the Coronation of Queen Elizabeth affect T.V?
6) How were viewers in Britain able to see events in the U.S.A.?
7) Which film started the growth of more cinemas in Britain?
8) What do you think has made films popular again?

1) Define the words:Satellite,wireless,commercial.
2) What evidence suggests radios were smaller after 1960?
3) Why do you think the first T.V. station was in London?
4) What drew more people to the cinema in the 1930's?

Use reference books to carefully illustrate and research:
1) The cartoon films of Walt Disney.
2) The life and work of John Logie Baird, the inventor of T.V.

Level 5

Sir Winston Churchill

In the 1930's Winston Churchill wanted Britain to be ready for war.

Churchill became Prime Minister in 1940.

Churchill visited the bombed houses to cheer up the people.

Churchill made many speeches on the Radio to cheer up people in Britain.

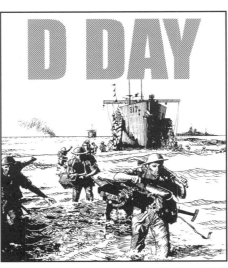

Churchill planned the D" day invasion of Europe in 1944.

Churchill was beaten by the Labour Party in the 194 election.

1) In 1930 Churchill wanted _____ to be ready for _____.

2) Churchill became _____ _____ in 1940.

3) Churchill visited the _____ houses to _____ up the people.

4) Churchill made many _____ on the _____ to cheer up people in Britain.

5) Churchill _____ the D day invasion of _____ in 1944.

6) Churchill was beaten by the _____ Party in the _____ election .

Level 2

Sir Winston Churchill

"Never in the field of human conflict was so much owed by so many to so few"

Winston Churchill had been a soldier, newspaper reporter, and politician since 1899. In the 1930's he opposed the striking miners. He wrote and printed a newspaper in the 1926 General Strike. Many workers hated him for his action. He wanted Britain to make weapons ready for war against Germany in the 1930's.

Churchill became Prime Minister in 1940. He made many Radio speeches to keep people's spirits up in the war. In 1940 Churchill visited the houses bombed by German planes in London to keep the people from losing hope. He planned bombing raids over German cities to smash Hitler's claims about how good the German air force was.

Churchill master minded the invasion of Europe in 1944, which led to victory over Germany in May 1945. Huge crowds cheered Churchill in London on V.E. day 1945. With the American and Russian leaders Churchill planned the future of Europe after the war. He was beaten in the 1945 election by the Labour party.

1) When did Churchill write and print a newspaper ?
2) When did Churchill want Britain to make weapons ready for war ?
3) Where did Churchill visit bombed houses in 1940 ?
4) What did Churchill plan to spoil Hitler's claims about the German Air force ?
5) What else did Churchill do in the war to keep people's spirits up?
6) When was the invasion of Europe master minded ?
7) Why was Churchill sad after the 1945 election ?

1) Why do you think many workers did not like Churchill in the 1930's?
2) Why do you think the crowds cheered Churchill on V.E.day ?

Carefully draw and colour your own picture of Churchill making a Radio speech during the war.

Level 3

Sir Winston Churchill

"LET US GO FORWARD TOGETHER"

Winston Churchill was a soldier and newspaper reporter in Africa from 1899 to 1905. He was a minister in the First World War and planned an attack in Turkey which cost thousands of soldier's lives. In 1926 he published a newspaper against the General Strike, and was against the miner's strikes in the 1930's, which annoyed the workers. Churchill wanted the government to build tanks, planes and ships to be ready for a war that the German leader Hitler was threatening. Churchill was a minister in the wartime government and became Prime Minister in 1940. He made many speeches on the Radio to encourage the people in hard times. When the German planes bombed London in 1940 Churchill would visit bombed homes to raise the people's spirits. He planned bombing raids on German cities to spoil the German leader Hitler's claims about his air force being unbeatable. Churchill worked hard to get loans from America to pay for arms and equipment for the war.

Churchill was the main planner behind the invasion of Normandy by Allied forces in June 1944, which was followed in May 1945 by the surrender of Germany. Churchill had planned the future of Europe with Roosevelt, the American president and Stalin the Russian Leader. But the Communist take overs of Eastern Europe led Churchill in 1947 to call this the "Iron Curtain between free and Communist Europe, a barrier of armed communist force". Churchill was beaten in the 1945 election by the Labour party, but was Prime Minister again from 1951-55.

A 1) When did Churchill become Prime Minister?
2) What did Churchill publish in 1926?
3) How did Churchill annoy workers in the 1930's?
4) Why did Churchill make many Radio speeches in the wartime?
5) Which action did Churchill take to spoil Hitler's claims about the German air force?
6) How did Churchill raise the spirits of the bombed people in London in 1940?
7) What was Churchill's part in the 1944 invasion of Europe?

B 1) What evidence suggests that Churchill was a good planner?
2) Why do you think Churchill talked about an Iron Curtain in Europe in 1947?
3) Why do you think workers disliked Churchill in the 1930's?
4) Why do you think Churchill wanted the government to build planes,ships and tanks in the 1930's?

5) Why do you think Churchill was both happy then sad in 1945?

C Carefully draw and colour your own picture of Churchill and the crowds on V.E.day in May 1945.

Level 4

Sir Winston Churchill

Winston Churchill was the son of a rich and famous politician. He served in wars in Africa as a soldier and newspaper reporter 1899-1905. He became an M.P. and a minister in the government in the First World War. He made a mistake sending troops to the Dardenelles, near Turkey then many men lost their lives. In 1926 he opposed the miner's strike and acted against the General Strike. He wrote, and printed the only newspaper published in the strike called the "British Nation". For this he was hated by many workers.

When in 1930 he read Adolf Hitler's book "Mein Kampf" and saw Hitler re-arming Germany he urged the British Government to stand firm and not allow the German leader to have any territory outside Germany. The Prime Minister Neville Chamberlain wanted to allow Hitler a little land thinking this would appease him. Churchill wrote newspaper articles urging the British government to build modern tanks, aeroplanes and ships. When in 1940 the German invasion of Norway had not been resisted enough by Prime Minister Chamberlain, Churchill became Prime Minister. He headed a government of all parties with the best brains from all sides to organise Britain's war effort.

He made many speeches on the Radio during the war, which helped keep up people's spirits. In the German "Blitz" bombing of London Churchill would tour the area, talk to the people, praise the rescue services and raise everyone's resolve to carry on. He planned night time bombing raids on Germany so that the claims of Hitler about the supreme German nation were challenged. He worked to get loans from America to pay for the war weapons. After the Americans joined the war in 1941 he worked with American President Roosevelt to plan the invasion of German Europe in 1944. He worked with the Russian leader Stalin and Roosevelt to plan the division of Europe after the war. On V.E. day June 1945 he received huge acclaim from the London crowds. But he and the Conservative were defeated in the 1945 General Election.

After this, Churchill felt let down, he spent time painting, building walls and writing a history of the war. In 1947 he made a speech about the communist take over of Eastern Europe saying that an "Iron Curtain" had split Europe. In 1951 he was again Prime Minister. At the Coronation of Queen Elizabeth II in 1953 he was made a knight. Old and ill in 1955 he resigned as Prime Minister. At his death in 1965 he had a State Funeral with leaders from all the World attending.

1) Why do you think the workers hated Churchill in the 1930's?
2) How did Churchill want Chamberlain to react to Hitler's plans in the 1930's ?
3) Which invasion led to Churchill becoming Prime Minister?
4) Why were Churchill's Radio speeches important in the war?
5) How did Churchill want the Americans to help in the war?
6) Why did Churchill plan bombing raids on Germany?
7) Which event made Churchill feel let down?
8) What do you think made Churchill call the communist take over of Eastern Europe an "Iron Curtain"?

1) Define the words:- appease; politician; communist.
2) What evidence suggests Churchill was good at talking to ordinary people?
3) Why do you think Churchill chose people from all parties to be in his wartime government?
4) What made Churchill resign as Prime Minister in 1955?

Use reference books to carefully illustrate and research:
1) The D day landings in Normandy 1944.
2) The life and work of either Adolf Hitler or Joseph Stalin.

Level 5

Time to Spare Activities

1. Interview a member of your family about their childhood.

2. List the equipment in your kitchen and compare it to the equipment in a 1930's kitchen.

3. Design an advertisement for a British factory to attract workers from India in the 1960's.

4. Research as much information as you can about the planes of the 2nd World War.

5. Design a Menu card for a Wartime Christmas dinner.

7. Write a letter from a Battle of Britain pilot to his family in August 1940.

8. Research as much as you can about Alexander Fleming's discovery of Penicillin.

9. Find out how to add up in pounds, shillings and pence.

10. Make a Britain Since 1930 timeline to display in your classroom.

11. Make a model of a 1940's aeroplane.

12. Write a letter from Winston Churchill to Stalin stating why he wants to be Russia's ally in 1941.

13. Make a timeline poster of different land transport vehicles since 1930.

14. Compare a 1930's map of your area with a present day map. List any changes you see.

15. Make a family tree for your family as far back as 1930.

16. Choose a year since 1930 and research as many facts or events as you can for the year.

17. List 10 items from 1940 that you would put into a time capsule.

18. Write a short play about an unemployed family in 1930.

19. Research the history of cinemas in your nearest town.

20. Design your own 1990's ideal home.

21. Research the life and space travel of Yuri Gagarin, the first space traveller.

22. Make a model of your favourite car since 1930.

23. Write a newspaper account of Man's first day on the Moon.

24. Make a collage model of a 1970's flower power person.

25. Design and make your own Space vehicle.

26. Make a 1950's kitchen in a shoe box.

27. Write a letter home from a tank commander in the North African campaign of 1942/3.

28. Write a diary of a Londoner in the Blitz for 3 Days.

29. Design your own clothes outfit for a 1960's Pop concert.

30. Make your own 1930's travel poster.

31. Research the life of someone famous in the 1960's.

32. Research as much as you can about the start of the National Health Service.

33. Make your own Prefabricated 1940's Bungalow in a shoebox.

34. Make a front page of your own Comic for the 1950's, with drawings and script.

35. Make a model of a 1930's aeroplane.

36. Research the story of your town in the Second World War.